THE PASTOR
OF THE LAST DAYS

THE VIRUS
ISRAEL ATTACKED!
GOD'S 12 MIRACULOUS RESPONSES

A NOVEL BY
PASTOR RICK A. BLOMGREN
WITH LELAND E. POUND

DEDICATIONS

To
My beloved Messiah Jesus the Christ.

To
My beloved Doc (1926-2016)

To
My beloved wife of 29 years, Jana

To
ALL MY CHERISHED READERS.
May you be encouraged and amazed at
what God the Father may soon show the world,
leading to a spectacular second coming of His Son.
The day Jesus arrives will be EPIC!

1

ISRAEL ATTACKED

THE SUNDAY - DAY ONE

A sudden loud knock on his study door startled Pastor Allen Rogers. What on earth? Joanne never bothered him while he worked on his Sunday morning message for the 10,000 worshipers at the Kingdom Today Center.

"I'm about done," he yelled.

"I turned on the TV a few minutes ago. You need to see this."

Allen wanted to brush away the intrusion into his early Sunday morning routine, sacrosanct in this household. An odd TV story didn't matter.

"Get out here now!" The edge in her voice surprised him, made him hesitate.

He stood. "Okay, okay," he said. "What's so important?"

He opened the door, his prerogative. She'd never think of opening it without asking.

"It's a breaking news alert," Joanne said. She held the clicker in her hand. "I'll fast backward so you can see it."

A solemn news reporter appeared on the screen. "A flash came in a minute ago," he said. "First reports say a major surprise attack on Israel occurred Sunday afternoon in the Middle East. Early reports from the Golan Heights and major Israeli border cities indicate large troop movements although we cannot confirm this information. Sketchy reports refer to missiles and war planes soaring over major Israeli cities. We'll be back with more."

Allen stared at the screen, while the news went to other stories. Odd, he thought. A major surprise attack on Israel?

"Now you know why I called you in," Joanne said. "What's your message topic this morning?"

"This news doesn't change what I plan to say. It's more important that since the Virus subsided, social distancing was suspended and churches started to congregate again, people's feelings remain unsettled as never before.

"I will continue my series about the new worldwide paradigm I see emerging and about my trepidations that many personal freedoms will never come back. Many believe the world needs to unify after surviving this earth-shattering pandemic. Christians and non-Christians alike continue the search for answers to the long-term question of why the Virus happened. Some wonder if it might be part of God's plan.

"I want to share how the pandemic fits into Bible prophecy but don't feel the time is right. Prophecy troubles many people and might exacerbate already raw nerves. For 35 years I've shied away from teaching prophecy in my church because I sensed my parishioners weren't interested, that they continue to want feel-good preaching. I know prophecy well, but I need to see a more solid sign from God before I venture into prophecy in our church.

"For now, I need to continue to emphasize God's love and comfort for us in these difficult times of rebuilding, which fits right in with what the current day Christian church needs."

Joanne turned off the television. "You don't need to justify yourself. You built a wonderful church and you've brought thousands of people to Jesus. You have been a great comfort to our congregation since the Virus. What more could you ask? I thought you'd be interested in the news."

"Of course, I'm interested. Honey, you know I do church this way to bring people in. They won't get the message if they don't come to church. We're helping God cleanse evil from the world and prepare the Kingdom of God here on earth so Jesus can return."

"If you truly feel that way," Joanne said, "why do you keep running your Thursday night study group where all you talk about is your hobby, Biblical end-time prophecies. Do you ever plan to include your knowledge of God's Biblical prognostications in your sermons?"

"I can't get into this subject today. In the Christian church nobody's interested, it'd kill my church and all the success I've built, my congregation will never stand for it. I made my decision a long time ago. I know what I'm doing. Maybe in the future I'll find an opening. I know God will show me when the time is right. Now is not the time."

"You came home so energized Thursday night."

Allen thought back to Thursday's meeting. It's true. He enjoyed his hidden passion for Biblical prophecy, fantasized at times about giving passionate sermons on this long discarded, almost forgotten subject matter. Okay, he lived for those meetings with his small intimate group of long-time friends who shared his love for the prophetic Bible teachings. He loved to talk on and on about the 24 major prophetic predictions his mentor Doc taught him so many years earlier and how it appears 12 have arrived and the final 12 are about to show up for mankind to literally witness soon. The message he crafted for this Sunday morning seemed like a lot of simplistic theology to offer comfort related to the world's new reality, to appeal to the modern psyche, a conundrum. Even preaching to 10,000 worshippers in his massive auditorium and to his nationwide television audience couldn't spark as much passion in him.

"I know. It's not time to spread the prophetic message yet. There's no audience for it."

"Think about what you heard on the news this morning."

"I'll start in good time," he said. "But not today. Let's eat breakfast. I need to be at Church early today."

†††✡†††

Pastor Allen Rogers stood off to the side of the massive stage at Kingdom Today Center in Northern Illinois, dressed in his casual short-sleeve collared shirt, jeans, and loafers. From the beginning of his formal ministry he discarded the old traditional Protestant ideas of ministerial robes and processionals down the center aisle of the church. In the enlightened world of contemporary Christianity, these old school rites no longer held any true meaning. Christianity evolved away from them.

The megachurch movement changed the way people looked at the Bible. When the older teachings outgrew their time, lost their effectiveness, a new way took over. Churches only needed to address issues which helped Jesus reestablish His Kingdom on earth, saw all else as irrelevant.

Allen glanced out at the crowd entering the center. His first thought this Sunday came out of nowhere, surprised him.

"Is this a church anymore?"

Most of the people sat too far away to recognize, most of them he'd never met, most of them he'd never meet. He felt real isolation on his stage, the bright lights that illuminated the stage for the TV cameras blinded him from seeing his audience, a necessary distraction so he could record his weekly message for airing the following week to a massive audience.

He enjoyed the jazzy music of the 10-member contemporary band that played at the side of the stage. Every megachurch these days featured a professional band, expensive but necessary to draw people, many of whom showed up for the concert, not the sermon. Again, his training told him the numbers validated the success of a ministry.

Five minutes to the nine-thirty start of the service. Band sounded great, the congregation filed in to take their seats like a sea of ants moving, shifting, sitting. With professional precision, the service always began on time and proceeded with no room for error. As always, he took pride in knowing the television recording to be aired the following week needed minimal editing.

This was success. Sure, he'd worked at it for 35 years. A group of parishioners hinted it might be time for him to retire. Nonsense. A youthful 60-year-old man, fit, with a full head of jet-black hair slightly greying at the temples, he didn't look his age. He preached with the effective fervor of a young man but with wisdom, experience, and deep Bible knowledge. He'd prove himself once again today. He'd give his parishioners what they wanted to hear, what they needed for this day, and they'd love him for it.

He designed his message for today on love, and how God provides comfort in times of trial and adversity to fit current times perfectly, a continuation of a series he shared as the world strained to rebuild after the Virus; every word of his sermon planned to the letter. Rebuilding remains a long arduous process.

He planned to include in his sermon today a widely accepted notion: God appointed Christians as His new chosen people to replace the Jews 2,000 years ago, in the time of Christ. Especially important in the times people lived in now, he needed to be among the ones to help provide comfort to the world. Oddly, this morning, Allen thought, do any of God's complete Biblical teachings indicate this replacement of the Jews concept as a possible truth? Judgments by God today don't match current day enlightenment, but didn't we just survive one? No. God is not a God of judgement but a God of compassion. No real hell, fire, and brimstone, which preachers used in the past as a cruel way to scare people into believing Jesus, existed. Many contemporary churches call the stories in the Old Testament allegorical, none of it relevant to today's enlightened worshippers. The Old Testament went out when the New Testament arrived, or did it?

Joanne got it wrong this morning. Allen knew for sure his people didn't want to hear about prophetic end-time predictions. Not the time, not the place. He seldom looked at the Old Testament. No, not true, he read those ancient pages for his Thursday night meetings, not for church. Teach the gospels, teach God's love and comfort in challenging times, not judgements or Old Testament prophecies.

Allen was never tempted to preach Biblical predictions in his church. He remembered when he was a member in his home church in Alabama, the pastor preached the whole Bible. The church never grew and eventually hundreds of parishioners drifted away. He didn't want to experience the fate of his old home church, so he searched for a new way to draw people. He studied megachurches and their simple but effective marketing, market research, contemporary bands and praise teams, radio then television ministries along with polling to find out what people wanted to hear in church. Ministry became a business.

He drifted away from Doc, his mentor thirty-five years ago. He loved Doc, enjoyed the meetings where he met John Josephs, his best friend, former Catholic seminarian, and a reluctant participant in Allen's megachurch. He respected John's views but noted even his friend reluctantly came to understand the megachurch way.

Nine-thirty on the dot the praise songs began. Allen sang them with the gusto he developed for the rest of the contemporary service. He felt the beat of the drums, the rhythm of the guitars pound into his body, watched the praise singers dance onto the stage, sing their hearts out. The crowd rose to their feet, roared in song. You did church this way.

Exactly at the fifteen-minute mark, a junior pastor stepped onto the stage, marched to the center microphone, shouted, "Welcome to the Kingdom Today Center!!!!"

Cheers and clapping erupted from the crowd. The pastor held up his hands, waited for the noise to die down.

"We gather here to worship God and praise Jesus Christ, our Savior, to savor the grace and love of God and the sacrifice His son Jesus Christ made to give us all everlasting life in Heaven. But first, I have a few announcements."

The junior pastor ran through the announcements, mostly routine matters like parking and where to find Sunday School classes, along with a few special programs coming up in the next week. The campus bustled with many activities and programs. Keep the congregation occupied, keep them present.

The junior pastor smiled, said, "God gives us abundance and now is the time to share the abundance you possess to support God's work here at Kingdom Today. Be generous as the ushers pass among you."

Like clockwork, an army of ushers marched up the aisles to predetermined positions from which they passed the offering plates down the aisles. The praise singers sang another two songs, accompanied by the band, while the ushers took the offering.

On completion of the offering, the junior pastor returned to the front of the stage. Behind him, two men brought the senior pastor's portable podium to the prominent midsection of the now deserted stage. "And now, it is my honor to introduce Kingdom Today's Senior Pastor, Allen Rogers!!"

Allen took a brisk walk across the stage towards his familiar podium, arms raised, to thunderous applause. He enjoyed the limelight, part of what made his job as a megachurch pastor so wonderful. A brief fleeting thought crossed his mind. Is it a sin to enjoy the fame? No, of course not, can't be, I'm doing God's work for our time. He's here to serve his people, exactly what he'd do today.

He arrived at his simple podium, a lonely monument on the vast stage. The audience lights dimmed. His image appeared on massive screens mounted above and to the sides of the stage, positioned so everyone in the crowd could see him. The TV cameras stationed around the auditorium, synchronized to perfection, started recording.

After offering an ebullient welcome to the massive crowd and TV audience, he noticed an odd movement at the back of the auditorium and hesitated. One of the entry doors in the back opened. A brilliant light from the doorway penetrated deep into the darkened auditorium, outlined the shadowy silhouette of a man standing in the doorway. The light intruding into the auditorium caught everyone's attention. A mysterious man entered the room. The man walked down the aisle in the dimly lit auditorium, slow, deliberate steps. Allen saw the audience turn to gaze at him in the silence. Odd, this never happened. Who was this stately man? Time seemed to stand still.

Allen noticed one prominent empty seat in the front row of the center section of the auditorium, directly below his podium, odd because all the front seats vanished the moment the crowd entered. The man continued his long walk down the wide center aisle to a hushed congregation. For a moment Allen felt silly standing in silence at the podium while this strange man walked down the aisle towards him.

The man seemed to know the seat waited for him. He walked with purpose into the bright stage lights.

A sudden shock of recognition. It's Doc, from thirty-five years ago, the man who taught him all he knew about Biblical end-times prophetic predictions. How did thirty-five years pass so fast? He didn't look a day older. Allen felt a sudden pang of pain. How could he neglect his old teacher for so many years? He couldn't remember hearing from Doc in decades. What prompted him to show up today of all days? He melted at Doc's bright smile. He loved Doc's insights and close friendship. Those bright blue eyes reminded him of the old days, when he studied in Doc's home at his round wood dining table, and at his office lined with towering shelves of reference books like a tight historical archive, where they talked and debated Biblical prophetic end-time predictions. He felt filled with joy. Doc reached the front of the auditorium, walked to the empty chair as if he knew it waited for him all along and sat down.

Allen realized the congregation fell silent during Doc's entrance. He felt like time disappeared and his last farewell to Doc happened a few minutes ago, not 35 years back. Why did he show up at this moment, of all days? The news story this morning? The attack on Israel? He knew the major prophetic predictions, all 24 of them, Doc taught him years ago.

He remembered the moment he said farewell to Doc, who smiled and said, "Remember the truths of Prophecy and God's plan for mankind. Remember!"

Why did Doc show up in his church today of all days after so many years? The newscast earlier in the morning haunted him. Did the Arabs finally attack Israel as prophesied in the Bible? Can't be, yet could the impossible have happened? Doc stared at him from the audience the moment he stood ready to deliver his prepared sermon. He felt the heat of Doc's eyes pierce him to the soul. He looked up at the congregation, seated in comfortable chairs, ready to receive his words.

Doc's teachings, the congregation, his prepared message, God's full Biblical 24-event Road Map[1] for the last days, the master of the universe's helper,[2] the Holy Spirit working on him at this moment, what's happening? Flash, flash, flash the images panned through his mind. Years of training, great fortune in creating one of the largest and most respected and viewed ministries in the region, was this all in God's plan for this moment?

The invasion. A lightning bolt of insight, the invasion, the pivotal Ezekiel[3] moment in Doc's explanations of God's predictions. Why else would Doc show up now if

---

[1] God's End times 24-event Road map is outlined on page 232.

[2] John 14:16

[3] Ezekiel 38:1 – 39:16 is the first of two wars listed in Ezekiel 38 and 39. One is instigated by God with a specific limited number of nations before the Tribulation. Ezekiel 39:17 -29, is a second different world war with Jesus at the end of the Tribulation including all remaining nations of the world. Two different wars.

not at the minute his explanation of God's final 12 end-time predicted events started to come true? The moment of truth arrived. The Virus terrified the world and brought mankind to their knees; a new reality set in, one where humanity would soon learn they needed God more than ever. This morning, Allen told Joanne he still wanted to see a large sign indicating the Virus might correlate with end time prophecy. God delivered this sign in today's news. The Virus recalibrated mankind's sensitivity to what was about to arrive. The world will soon discover that today's attack on Israel will make the Virus event pale by comparison. The invasion this morning was God's next major sign, the thirteenth end-time prophecy in His 24-event Road Map that will lead the world towards the day of the Lord's return. Today we witnessed the arrival of God's prophesied Ezekiel moment!

Doc continued to smile at him.

Allen knew one truth. He could no longer deliver his planned message with passion, it seemed trite and passé, like rotten leftovers hidden deep in the refrigerator. He looked at Doc, then prayed silently, *dear Holy Spirit, please give me guidance in this moment of truth.*

He felt the Holy Spirit of God well up inside him. With sudden clarity he saw the major prophecy fulfilled by God Himself this morning in Israel, stared out over the thousands of people awaiting his trite words of feel-good comfort preaching. Not today, not with Doc and God standing here with him this blessed morning. He knew what he needed to do, felt confident and empowered.

The Pastor of the last days was about to arrive!!!

2

ALLEN MEETS DOC

Forty-two years earlier, Allen wasn't invited to the party hosted by the History of Faith Department for certain students and faculty at his seminary. With limited funds as a first-year seminarian, how could a young bold pastor trainee resist the lure of refreshments and rousing music when the event took place across the courtyard from his campus dormitory in the main dining area at Clove Port Seminary in Kentucky. No, the party didn't honor his History of Faith professor, the Seminary held it for another teacher, a man he barely knew, who taught the book of Revelation in a senior level class. John's esoteric book of predictions fascinated Allen, but he never studied it.

What the heck, crash the party and see what happens.

He walked in like an invited guest, ignored the sign-in desk, walked over to the refreshment table with food on his mind. Great spread for a seminary, mostly healthy food like veggies and lemonade to drink.

He noticed an older man at the end of the table, handsome, well-trimmed silver hair, about sixty or so years old, dressed in a dark suit with a blue tie. Allen seemed uncertain about what to do next. He guessed later the uncertainty made him walk over to the man and say,

"Hello, I'm Allen Rogers, first year student here. You look a little lost."

The man looked up at him. Allen gazed at him, saw a depth in the dark blue eyes he couldn't penetrate. The man smiled.

"I'm Doc," he said. "Visiting an old friend here. The guy who teaches Revelation."

"I might take his class someday. Always found the subject interesting."

"Tell me about yourself," Doc said.

This man's forward, no small talk, right into the meat.

"I'm a student, studying contemporary worship. I want to bring God and Jesus to masses of people, but I can't do it like the traditional church I grew up in. It's collapsing from lack of attendance. I want to do it different."

"Did your minister preach the Bible?"

"Every Sunday. When I was a kid, people packed the sanctuary. Later the crowd began a slow decline. He talked a lot about the prophetic predictions found throughout the Bible, Old and New Testaments. I never figured out why he didn't attract more people."

Doc looked down, as if saddened by the problem. "Mr. Rogers, I'm afraid the Christian churches today, the vast majority of them, fell away from deep faith and truth,[4] lost their connection with Jesus and turned to the worldly needs of people, in grave error."[5]

"They teach a new way to grow churches," Doc said. "They emphasize size over substance and use the number of parishioners to claim a successful ministry for God. Lots

---

[4] 1 Timothy 4:1, 2 Timothy 4:3-4, *Stunned*, 2015, Blomgren, Page 37
[5] 1 John 2:18-19, *Stunned*, 2015, Blomgren, Page 176

of large churches spring up and draw thousands of people with contemporary music. They emphasize the love God bestows on humanity. They strive to get away from the Old Testament with its predictions for the world and what they mean. They considered talk of judgments and hell old school that scare people away. Today's church takes what God says out of context. They're not willing to give God credit for the blessings He gives through them. Seems like a great formula for growth but flawed."

"Mr. Rogers, are you interested in God's Biblical prophetic predictions for the end times?

"Of course, always found them fascinating. People don't want to listen anymore. By the way, call me Allen."

"Allen, we're in the last days in an age of apostasy.[6] Many churches today are falling away from true faith.[7] This holds in today's seminaries too. They mean well but they don't teach the correct interpretation tools required to understand Biblical illuminations accurately. They claim inerrancy of the Bible to be incorrect and say the Bible contains many errors. This grieves God. Churches for centuries added and subtracted passages from the Bible, an explicit violation of God's divine copyright stated clearly at the end of the last chapter in the book of Revelation. There are grave penalties for this error in judgment.[8]

"I teach Biblical prophecy to a small group of students. I've identified twenty-four major end-time prophecies or predicted events which indicate we truly live in the last

---

[6] 2 Timothy 4:3-4, 2 Thessalonians 2:1-3
[7] 1 Timothy 4:1
[8] Revelation 22:18-19

days. We know this because God already fulfilled 11 of the 24. We witnessed them. Would you like to join us next Wednesday evening?"

"Where do you meet?"

"My home, 7 Augury Place, 7 p.m. Be there."

Allen said, "I'll be there."

"I knew you would," Doc said. "See you Wednesday."

The man pulled his jacket tight around his body, walked to the door of the reception area, turned, smiled at Allen, then left.

✝✝✝✝✝✝✝

Allen rang the doorbell at Doc's house the next Wednesday night. Doc answered, invited him in.

"You're early," he said. "The others will arrive in fifteen minutes or so."

Allen checked his watch, 7 p.m. "I thought I got here on time."

"You did, my time. Come in, take a seat. I like to get to know new people in my group before I introduce them to all the members. Tell me, what brought you to seminary training?"

"I watched the only church I ever knew die away as I grew up. So many of my old friends either left the church or moved on to larger churches in the city. My pastor was a Biblical sage with lots of training and experience. I loved his sermons. He talked about prophecies, about how we needed to get right with God in this life. Yes, he talked about judgments, said the last days were near. The

16

prophecies fascinated me, but he never got into too much detail and believed many of them already happened."

"Allen, so many pastors see the same events. What does your seminary teach you about the Bible?"

"It's the Word of God."

Allen waited through a moment of silence, as if Doc wanted him to say more. "A lot of the stories are allegory, one way to get the Word of God across."

"They say many of the events recorded didn't happen, they're made-up stories to think about?"

"A lot of it isn't relevant today." Allen felt Doc's blue eyes stare at him. "I mean it's relevant but doesn't work today. God wants people to join His churches, the more the better, to accept Jesus and follow His teachings about love in their everyday lives. Whatever truth they believe becomes an individual choice. I want to bring the Gospel to thousands of people, not a few dozen, so I need to selectively skirt around certain Biblical truths that annoy many Christians today."

"Do you believe God wrote the Bible himself, exactly the way he wanted it?" Doc said. "Allen, nothing's changed in the two thousand years since Jesus walked the Earth and promised to return. God finished the Bible, the perfect completed Bible, in its current form almost two thousand years ago. God is perfect,[9] does not err, nor does he put untrue or irrelevant items in His written Word."[10]

Allen looked away. "Do you have water?" he asked.

While Doc went to the kitchen for water, Allen absorbed Doc's words. Of course, God's Word is inerrant

---

[9] Matthew 5:48
[10] Hebrews 6:18

and truth. He used stories to make His points, like all ancient writings. They work, he saw the results from his classes and from practice sermons he preached. People today required a softer, more simplified approach, not the prophecies of his youth. His own dying church proved this idea.

Doc returned with a glass of water and a paper napkin, handed it to Allen, sat down, leaned forward to listen.

"I want to bring the Gospel to as many people as possible," Allen said. "The old ways don't work today. I do hope when God brings prophecy to a certain point, I'll introduce the deeper truths of the Bible to them."

"And how long do you feel this might take?"

"I'm here to listen to you, to learn more about Biblical prophetic end-time predictions."

The doorbell rang. "They're arriving," Doc said. "Listen and learn tonight, ask questions if you want." Doc stood, walked to the door, opened it.

"Ahhh, John, great to see you tonight. I want you to meet a new friend."

Allen stood.

Doc said, "John Josephs, meet Allen Rogers. He's studying at the local Seminary to be a pastor. He's interested in joining our study group. I don't sense he knows what we talk about."

"I'm sure I'm about to find out." Allen smiled. "How did you get involved here, John?"

"I met Doc five years ago after I left Catholic Seminary. I came from a large Catholic family, so they criticized me when I decided not to complete my priesthood studies. I found their rituals and teachings disingenuous and not fully Bible based. Doc's teachings about the Bible contained powerful material I never heard in church."

Doc said, "The others will arrive soon. Enjoy some refreshments."

Allen watched John fill his plate with a cookie or two and three apple quarters, sit down on the couch. He took his time with his own refreshments, then sat beside John. "I never knew much about Catholicism. What made you leave?"

John stared off into the distance, as if looking for the right words. "I don't want to hurt anyone. My family has been Catholic for centuries. They seemed happy to be taught rather than explore their own illuminations of the Bible with the help of the Holy Spirit. The church never encouraged personal Bible reading. Priests claimed the masses could not understand many passages in the scriptures so as trained priests they presented the correct interpretations so everyone could follow the rules of the church. I presume you've never attended a Catholic Mass."

"Correct. I hear they perform a lot of rituals, repeat a lot of statements."

John continued, "The feeling inside a Catholic church is one of reverence, quiet, ceremony. I saw the paintings, the statues, the gold and silver décor, the priests in their grand robes and I asked myself if religion amounted to this and little else. I saw little connection to Christ and God, the personal connection I craved. I couldn't find it studying to become a priest."

"How did you react?"

"The church told me how to communicate with God. They say becoming a priest brings you closer to God. For me, the priesthood pushed me away. I never felt comfortable with the rules and obligations. After reading the Bible myself, I found a major disconnect between what the church said and what the Bible tells us. I left to find the God my Catholic heritage never let me find. I attended many Protestant churches, but none touched what I searched for. Maybe I didn't know at the time what I wanted. I felt God pulled in an odd direction. Then I met Doc."

Allen glanced at Doc, now welcoming a few other people into his house. He saw a graciousness he'd never seen before. Doc welcomed his guests, made them feel comfortable, but let Allen talk with John as if he knew the conversation was the most important gift he could give the two of them. How he knew, Allen didn't understand.

Doc closed the door behind the last guest, turned to face the small group of people in the room. The sounds of greeting and welcome softened, then disappeared. Allen felt Doc's commanding presence, as apparently did the others.

"Everyone please stand and hold hands in a circle." He paused for a moment. *"Heavenly Father bless everyone who gathers here in Your name and presence. Help them to hear the truth of Your holy word as given by You to Your prophets in ancient times that we may better understand Your plan for humanity and specifically Your glory-the Jews.[11,12] In the name of Jesus Christ our Savior, Amen."*

---

[11] Isaiah 46:13, 48:11, Glory
[12] Isaiah 43:20-21, Jews are the chosen people of God

Allen opened his eyes. Doc's prayer soothed him in a way he didn't comprehend in the moment. He felt peace, as if he found a home that he never knew he needed. He and the others took seats at Doc's large round dining room table. Doc sat in his comfortable chair facing the group. Nobody talked.

"We welcome a new guest here tonight," Doc said. "Please welcome Allen Rogers, a local seminary student I met a few days ago. He's interested in learning more about God's 24 Biblical prophetic end-time predictions. Tonight, for Allen's benefit, we will discuss God's first eleven major end-time prophecies that the Lord already fulfilled, the ones we witnessed as they started to arrive in 1914. I'm certain we'll see new insights in them for all of you."

This confused Allen. Eleven of twenty-four prophecies already fulfilled? In all his studies, nobody ever claimed this. They mentioned the formation of the new State of Israel,[13] an obvious big one, but eleven in total completed? He leaned forward to hear more, intrigued.

Doc spoke first. "In the Bible, God makes it clear the Bible is perfect. God makes it clear we must study the entire Bible in context, not bits and verses we happen to like.[14] The Bible tells us God's prophets, all of them, spoke as real God-inspired men[15] and He created a specific design for His chosen people, the Hebrews. Events will happen to fulfill certain end-time predictions laid out in the Bible in clear words. People often refuse to listen to these predictions or discount them or misunderstand

---

[13] Matthew 24:32-34 *"fig tree,"* Isaiah 66:8
[14] 2 Timothy 3:16-17
[15] 2 Peter 1:20-21

them. Be clear, God tells us the Bible contains all we need to know if we but read and understand with the guidance of the Holy Spirit, our helper. The Bible predicts twenty-four specific events to happen by design as signs for us to witness in the last days. They lead us to signs God wants us to see and understand for a purpose, which will take place the day the Lord returns to take believers home with him. But the Bible says nobody knows the day or hour of the Lords return.[16] There is much more to this and it is incredible.[17],[18],[19]

That's not what Allen's professors in seminary taught. The students learned most of the prophetic predictions in the Bible came true in ancient times and don't apply to the present. Yet Doc's words made sense in a strange way, like a splash of cold water in his face.

"John," Doc said, "would you outline the first set of eleven fulfilled end-time prophecies for us?"

"Yes, Doc. I will. Remember, God warned us in Revelation to never add or subtract anything to or from the Bible,[20] which means all the words found therein carry significance. He tells us we will see wars and rumors of wars, famines, and earthquakes, which warn us of the beginning of birth pangs[21] that specifically relate to the rebirth of the new State of Israel in one day.[22]"

"Very good overview," Doc said. "Please continue, John."

---

[16] Matthew 24:36
[17] Philippians 2:5-11 Jesus gives up certain heavenly knowledge as a man
[18] John 17:1-5 After ascension Jesus gets full authority back, He knows everything
[19] *Stunned* 2015, Blomgren, Page 332
[20] Revelation 22:18-19
[21] Matthew 24:4-8, *Stunned*, 2015, Blomgren, Pages 12-13
[22] Isaiah 66:7-8, *Stunned,* 2015, Blomgren, Pages 95-96

"As I understand from the Bible, the first prophecy relates to the two end-time birth pangs explained in the book of Matthew.[23] They start with World War I in 1914[24] and finish with World War II from 1939 to 1945.[25] The impact of these wars led to the formation of the of the new State of Israel in 1948. WWI made the land ready for the Jews, WWII made the Jews ready for their new homeland. God knew both birth pangs needed to happen for Israel's primary benefit."

Allen never heard this before, but in a way, it made sense. "Excuse me, I get the rebirth of Israel, we knew about that prediction. The wars? They're new to me."

"Follow the pattern as we outline it," Doc said. "God will reward your patience."

John said, "Once you see the pattern, the rest will become evident. Obviously, Israel plays a pivotal role in all of God's end-time prophecies. Doc, please explain more clearly for Allen."

"Remember, God always claimed the Jews as His chosen people," Doc said. "In Isaiah He calls them His glory[26] and says He will never give His glory to another.[27] Therefore, all the early prophecies pertain to Israel to this day.

"The second prediction says God will prepare the land of Israel for the Jews, evidenced by the British Balfour Declaration in 1917.[28] This resulted from an amazing set of

---

[23] Matthew 24:4-8, *Stunned*, 2015, Blomgren, pages 32-33
[24] *Stunned*, 2015, Blomgren, pages 32, 90-94
[25] *Stunned*, 2015, Blomgren, pages 93-94
[26] Isaiah 46:12
[27] Isaiah 48:11
[28] *Stunned*, 2015, Blomgren, page 33

events in WWI. At the end of the war, England, which controlled the land area known today as Israel, officially prepared the land for the Jews[29] when they declared the right for Israel to at a future time reform a national homeland for Jewish people in this land."

"I see," Allen said.

"The third prediction covers the formation of the United Nations in 1945.[30],[31] The Bible says in Luke when we see the fig tree bud (Israel) and all the trees put forth leaves, (the United Nations) we know the time of the end nears.[32] This organization became critical to the establishment of Israel as a new world nation."

"The fourth prediction?" Allen asked.

"You're learning."

"But you said we've seen eleven fulfilled end-time predictions."

"In good time." Doc shifted in his chair. "Let's talk about the fourth prediction, the reestablishment of the reborn State of the Israel in 1948, which the United Nations ratified. This is the birth, the first super sign[33] of three God gave us in His twenty-four prophetic events Road Map.

"In the fifth prediction or prophecy the return of the Jews to the Holy Land begins, accelerating in 1948. In this second exodus God brings all His people, the Jews, back to Israel from where he scattered them after the destruction of the second Temple in 70 AD.[34]

---

[29] Zephaniah 2:1-2 gather yourselves together, *Stunned* 2015, Blomgren, page 33.

[30] Luke 21:29-32, the fig tree is Israel, all the trees the United Nations

[31] *Stunned*, 2015, Blomgren, page 34

[32] Luke 21:32, *Stunned*, 2015 Blomgren page 34

[33] Matthew 24:32-34, *Stunned*, 2015, pages 34-35, 94-95

[34] Jeremiah 31:8, Zephaniah 2:1-2, Ezekiel 37:11-14, *Stunned*, 2015, Blomgren, pages 35-36

"The sixth event marks the capture of Jerusalem by the Jews in Israel's six-day war in 1967, fulfilling the completion of the time of the gentiles."[35]

John said, "Allen, I know this is new to you. We know many prophecies exist in the Bible and we have a lot more detail about how all of them play out. You need to be patient with us because in time, with detailed study of each, they will become clear to you."

"I'm beginning to see an integration pattern," Allen said. "What a fascinating way to study the Bible. What are the next five prophecies? I never equated any of this as possibilities tying together so precisely. This is amazing!!"

John said, "To be brief, the seventh event outlines severe worldwide apostasy,[36] where many Christians fall away from the faith and teachings of their fathers the prophets regarding Jesus and Jews. Europe is secular now and many churches here in the United States preach watered-down theology. Allen, you've seen this in seminary, how many professors water down the teachings, how much of the Bible is not taught, how the Old Testament is neglected.

"The eighth prediction emphasizes the rapid increase in travel and knowledge.[37] We see this every day with airplanes, freeways, computers and cell phones."

"The last three prophecies or events may feel esoteric," Doc said, "but I assure you they aren't. They're critical to the events to follow soon.

---

[35] Luke 21:24, *Stunned*, 2015, Blomgren, Page 36
[36] 2 Thessalonians 2:1-3, 1 Timothy 4:1, 2 Timothy 4:3-3, Hebrews 5:11-14, *Stunned*, 2015, Blomgren, pages 36-38
[37] Daniel 12:4, *Stunned*, 2015, Blomgren, pages 38-39

"Number nine is a severe rise in Anti-Semitism.[38] This is not Nazi Germany and individual hatred, this is the hatred by the Arabs and much of the world today towards the new State of Israel and all Jews which they consider a threat to their control of the Middle East and the world.

"The tenth is the ability to implement the future Mark of the Beast, the rise of sophisticated technology.[39] This one is a worldwide proliferation, visible in plain sight yet hidden from the untrained.

"Number eleven predicts Israel dwelling securely in the Holy Land, as they do today in unwalled villages.[40]

"The twelfth prophecy says Israel will abandon Gaza soon.[41]

"The fourth prediction, the rebirth of the State of Israel, sets the final generational timeclock of the last days.[42] A generation may be defined as 100 years per a reading in Genesis 15.[43] In Matthew 24:34, the Bible indicates 'this final generation will not pass away until all these events take place.' Based on the birth of Israel, God intended for us to recognize this as His Biblical final generation, which could span up to 100 years.

"How might we know Israel holds the key to starting the end-times generation? Let's assume for a moment the State of Israel is a living person. Look at Israel as a Jewish man, growing up from an infant into manhood. In Isaiah,[44]

---

[38] Psalm 83:1-4, *Stunned*, 2015, Blomgren, page 39
[39] Revelation 13:15-18, *Stunned*, 2015, Blomgren, pages 39-40
[40] Ezekiel 38:8, 11, 14, *Stunned*, 2015, Blomgren, pages 40-41
[41] Zephaniah 2:3-4, *Stunned*, 2015, Blomgren, pages 41-42, fulfilled in 2005
[42] Matthew 24:34, Luke 21:3, *Stunned*, 2015, Blomgren pages 95-96
[43] Genesis 15:12-16, 400 years Egyptian captivity, freed in the 4th generation so we can infer a generation is 100 years.
[44] Isaiah 66:7-8

God shares about a future birth that relates to Israel. In Isaiah we hear about the birth of a 'man child' *(Greek 'genea' = born one)* and a 'land born in one day.' We witnessed this. Based on the life cycles of a Jewish human male, amazing historical events and timing occurred since Israel's May 14, 1948 rebirth.[45]

"The rebirth of the State of Israel started a generational time clock. It started a literal timeline that all Christians who love the study of end-time prophecies need to understand. God graciously provided additional indications, all amazing, to validate this.

"Symbolically, on May 14, 1948, the date of Israel's rebirth, a few of the surrounding enemy Arab countries became highly irritated. They decided to fight against Israel on day one of the new country's existence and promised to take it down fast. Their efforts failed. This irritating action symbolically relates to a Jewish boy's circumcision.

"A Jewish boy becomes responsible for his actions, accountable, at 13 years of age. He becomes a Bar Mitzvah. The Jewish people hold a Bar Mitzvah ceremony for the young man to celebrate this milestone. In WWII, a German, Karl Adolf Eichmann, became the chief architect of the Holocaust. He escaped at the end of the war and hid as a fugitive until his capture by the Israelis in 1960. On December 15, 1961, a court in Israel sentenced him to death and held him 'accountable' for the deaths of millions of Jews. Israel was thirteen years and seven months old when this happened. Israel celebrated this verdict.

---

[45] These events are all true in the real world today.

"A Jewish man becomes eligible to fight in wars while in his 20th year of life (*after his 19th birthday*). Adding 19 years to 5-14-1948, we get 5-14-1967. On 6-7-1967 (*Israel was 19 years and 23 days old*), Israel fought and won the Six-Day War and the City of Jerusalem returned to the control of the Jewish people . . . after more than 1,900 years in exile — a fulfillment of prophecy.[46]

"In the life of a Jewish man, he becomes a man of peace at the age of 30. Jesus, our Rabbi Messiah Jesus, started His formal ministry at 30 years of age. Thirty years added to 5-14-1948 equals 5-14-1978. In September 1978, when Israel was 30 years and 4 months old, it negotiated the Camp David Peace Accords. Then, in March 1979 (*Israel was 30 years and 10 months old*), Egypt and Israel, brokered by Jimmy Carter, signed the Camp David Peace (*security*) Accords. This plan made it possible to keep the borders with Israel and its neighbors safe by agreement — another fulfillment of prophecy.

"Israel will turn 100 years of age in May 14, 2048, our window for all end time events to take place. We've many years left, but these events could all occur in your lifetimes.

"The book of Luke directs us watch what is going on in the world and correctly analyze the present time in which we live.[47] This is why prophecy is so important.

"We are, clearly, in the 'season' of the Lord's return. Utilizing the possible full 100 years from Genesis 15:12-16 and calculating the rebirth of Israel started the 'final

---

[46] Luke 21:24, Jerusalem no longer trampled under the foot of the Gentiles
[47] Luke 12:54-56, emphasis on verse 56

generation,'[48] God might be telling us a lot regarding this final generation."

"Doc, what you shared is incredible!" Allen said. "I never heard of most of these prophecies or the analysis of the final generation. What you say makes amazing sense. How did I miss these prophecies for so long?"

"I'm here to open your eyes to see God's truth," Doc said. "God is gracious and says to us in the book of John, *'He tells us about events before they happen so when they happen, we may believe.'*[49] I welcome you to join this group in earnest, to meet with us each week, learn about these prophetic predictions in detail to understand in depth what God shared with us in advance so we can better prepare for Jesus' return. Allen, I see important events in your future. God guided you here, let us guide you in His ways for a while. For now, it's time to go home, read our Bibles, and pray about the future."

"I'll be here next week, ready to learn more," Allen said. "But can you answer one question?"

"Of course."

"How did you learn all of this? I've studied the Bible for years but never saw any of the prophecies you talked about line up in the spectacular way you explained briefly tonight, most of them are new to me."

Doc stood silent for a moment, as if pondering what to say next. "I studied the Bible for many years and consulted God for guidance. He led me to the right passages and their logical purposeful sequences. With the help of the

---

[48] Luke 21:21:32, this generation will not pass away until all these things take place. All these things are God's 24 prophecies as explained in this book.
[49] John 14:29, also Mark 13:23

29

Holy Spirit the truths of the Bible and of God's prophecies or predictions became clear and obvious. You'll see this as we go through the discussions each week. Trust God the Father, Jesus the Christ His Son and the Holy Spirit and you will see the truth. I'm glad you're staying with us."

What a contrast to Allen's seminary teachings!

††††††

The following week, Allen listened to Professor Milton in his seminary church building class with intent attention, watched for the areas where his teaching meshed with Doc's analysis of the Bible, found little.

He raised his hand. Professor Milton recognized him. "You want to ask a question?"

"You keep saying we need to move past old ways of teaching to attract more people to church. What about the Old Testament and the prophets? Aren't they relevant today?"

Professor Milton said, "We've gone over this before. The authors of the Old Testament wrote for a small, pastoral group of people with little understanding of the evolution of earth and the universe. For centuries people treated much of the Old testament as allegorical, where the stories illustrate points through fiction. If you want to grow a church, deemphasize the old teachings because people will not respond to them well in today's world. Church growth validates Christianity's success in the world today. Christians replaced Jews as God's chosen people two thousand years ago, which makes the Old testament irrelevant in today's enlightened societies.

"What about the book of Revelation?" Allen asked.

Professor Milton looked surprised at being questioned like this. "It's allegory, not literal. In ancient times church leaders didn't support it much. Mr. Rogers, can we continue this discussion in private?"

"Of course. Your office after class?"

††††††

Half an hour later, Allen stepped into Professor Milton's tiny office, one room with a desk and several file cabinets, no bookshelves, austere ... cold.

"Please, take a seat," the professor said.

"Thank you. I see a lot of difficulties with your ideas about how to grow churches. Then I remember my old church in Alabama, which, about 10 years ago, started to lose parishioners. My pastor tried all the methods he knew, preached with the vigor he always showed but people drifted away. I never could figure out why."

"Did he preach from the Old Testament a lot?"

"A lot of the time. A lot about judgement and how we need to get on God's right side to succeed in life. Leads to my question, why did the people leave?"

Professor Milton leaned back in his chair. "Let me tell you about God. He welcomes new people into his church. He wants growth, He wants people to hear the message of His love for mankind and how Christians became His new chosen people. Jesus came to save everybody, the Jews missed their chance, Christianity took the new higher place with God."

"In order to reach people, you go where they live and meet them at their own level to help God create His Kingdom on earth, our assignment in these last days. Most people in America and the world today know little about the Bible, we need to teach them the correct reading. They may remember stories from Sunday School, but see the basic message of Jesus as love. God wants everyone converted to Christian teachings. God accepts them even if they don't like the old Biblical teachings. It's okay with Him, at least people learn His basic message. God doesn't care about the rest in the scheme of life, only love matters."

Allen said, "I'm studying to become a minister because I want to reach people with the accurate complete message of Jesus Christ. How can I do it correctly? Professor Milton, I believe we must teach certain truths in the Bible. God drew up a far greater plan for mankind that involves the Jews as well as His love for those who accept Christ. Jesus and all the apostles lived as Jews and never gave up their heritage, which holds special significance. Jesus commanded the apostles to go out and preach to the Jews first, in the synagogues,[50] for a purpose. I see much more in the story. I can't reach many people in a tiny church in a small town. Yet I see value in the old teachings and in the prophetic predictions outlined in the Bible. How can we ignore them?"

"Allen, they aren't relevant in the modern age; we've moved past the old allegories," Professor Milton said.

---

[50] Acts 13:5, 13, 42,46, 14:1, 17:1,17, 18:4-11, 19:8, 28:17, 28:28, *Stunned*,2015, Blomgren, pages 292-293

"Aren't you watering down God's possible intended message, making modern day ministry a feel-good process?"

"People want to feel good these days. They don't want to hear about sin, about hell, about punishment and judgement. People don't like pastors to scare them today. Give people what they want. Many people don't accept the entire Bible as accurate so let them accept the pieces they like, discard the ones they don't, why disrupt their apple carts, it doesn't matter."

"So, you say the old ways worked in their time, but they'd kill the modern contemporary church today."

"Exactly. We must teach a kind, merciful, loving God. I repeat, we can't scare people these days, which means the Old Testament doesn't work anymore. Keep listening in class and you'll see how this new better way works. Look at the proof around you. Huge churches spring up all over the country, reach thousands of people with God's message of love, a success I know you want to join in. Teach the parts of the Bible today's people want to accept, not the old version and the old books, they aren't relevant. You'll do fine if you do."

"Thank you, professor," Allen said. "I'll take your thoughts into consideration."

††††††††

Allen looked forward to lunch with Doc at least once a month. He argued and questioned every point Doc made, got straight answers from Doc, many of which he didn't want to hear. After five years of seminary and Doc's teachings, he faced a dilemma, a crisis of conscience. His mentor Doc and seminary professors taught two diametrically opposed views of the ministry for the current age. This created a conflict for him.

Doc acted his usual ebullient self this noon. Allen saw him as a second father, a mentor who pulled him back to the narrow road of God's plan for humanity.

Allen said, "I'm almost ready to graduate from seminary and find a church to lead. I want to build a large church to bring the Word of God to as many people as possible."

"I hope I've enlightened you well enough for your task."

"I love your teachings, Doc. I'm running into a lot of trouble figuring out how to proclaim them in today's world."

"Tell me what you plan to do."

Allen stared into Doc's eyes, saw them filled with love but also with fierce passion. How could he say what he needed to say in this great man's presence? How much would it hurt him?

"I want to start with the loving God of the New Testament, proclaim the teachings of Jesus as the Savior of mankind and teach how we must love each other. This message will draw crowds."

"How would you introduce the Biblical prophetic predictions you've learned into this love-filled process?"

"I don't know yet."

"Allen, let me say a few words to remind you of where God stands in this situation. He wrote the Bible, make no mistake, the author is God no matter how many human hands He used. He placed in this one book all we need to know to live purposeful Christian lives and all we need to know to accept and welcome the return of Jesus Christ to this world in the last days."

"I know."

"God designed His book as a Road Map for us. As I taught multiple times, in Revelation He warns us to not take away or add any words to any portion of the Bible or face severe penalties."[51]

"I'm not changing the Bible. I'm not teaching parts of it yet."

"Is there a difference? Aren't selective omissions taking away from truth?"

"Each generation interpreted the Bible differently, saw some parts as more important than others and preached accordingly. I want to bring people together around the parts of the Bible they understand then to add more parts later when I feel they're receptive. I won't ignore any part of the Bible. Churches that preach about coming punishments, that show a God of judgement that gave us predictions about the coming of Jesus when they are told nobody can know the exact day and hour of His return are dying out. We stand to lose Christianity itself."

"Allen, God never changes. He is the God of the Old Testament, of the New Testament. He developed a plan for humanity, for His chosen people, the Jews, as we discussed so many times in our group. You know the theology behind the prophetic predictions, you know how they began to come true in our day, how the day of the Lord nears. God told us in the Bible about future events

---

[51] Revelation 22:18-19

before they happen so when we see them happen, we will believe."[52]

"I need to make my own way," Allen said.

"I know you do. I continue to believe God created an amazing plan for your life. You may not know it yet, but He will support you when the time comes for you to act for Him. I support you in whatever you do, knowing you desire to serve the greater Glory of God in the process. Follow your heart, go into the world, build your church to as much greatness as you can manage. God will show you what comes next. Remember the truths of Prophecy and God's plan for mankind. Remember!"

††††††††

Allen graduated from seminary two months later. At the next meeting of the group a few days after his graduation, Allen said, "I'm ready to start my new ministry. World, here I come!"

Doc said, "I've enjoyed working with all of you for the past five years. With a sad heart, I'm moving away and must end our group meetings together. I've received a new assignment which will take a lot of my time."

Allen said, "Sad news. I hoped we could stay in touch."

"We will, for a while," Doc replied.

John said, "We love you and your teachings, Doc. Thank you for all you've done for us."

Allen said, "This is a sad day. Thank you, Doc, for our incredible years together. I know more about Biblical prophecy than I ever expected."

---

[52] John 14:29

††††††

Allen trusted John's wisdom almost as much as Doc's. After the first group meeting five years before, Allen talked with John as often as possible, so much they became good friends. John married Alice soon after he left the Catholic seminary. They were raising four young children. After Doc left for his new assignment, he and John spent many hours together each week at work on the chronological Biblical puzzle Doc's end time predictions created.

††††††

About a month after graduation from seminary, John and Alice invited Allen out to dinner. John said, "Do you mind if we bring a girlfriend of Alice's along?"

"Of course not," Allen said.

They decided to meet at the Seafood Palace on Main Street, one of the hot spots in town. Allen arrived early, found a table for four, waited. Since he completed his seminary training, he suspected he'd take a junior pastor role before he stepped into a senior pastor position. He noted all the go-getters who started their own church right out of school. They'd write a book or find great Christian radio bookings to get a fast start.

Don't envy them, he cautioned himself. Have faith in the will of God to send him in the right direction, where he'd make the biggest difference. No idea where. His thoughts of finding a church consumed his mind. He thought to himself, stop obsessing this evening, concentrate on Alice's friend.

He looked forward to dinner, to meeting Alice's friend.

John and Alice walked into the restaurant. Behind them Allen saw a young woman in a conservative dress with dark brown hair. She looked about his age.

Allen stood, shook hands with John and Alice. Alice said, "This is Joanne, one of my best friends. She's a third-year student at the local University and we thought you two might like to meet."

"It's my pleasure to meet you, Joanne," Allen said. He smiled at her beauty, felt an immediate attraction.

Joanne sat across from him at the table, ordered salmon for dinner. Allen ordered halibut. Joanne seemed to share the attraction, started the conversation, "John said you worked with him in Doc's prophecy group." She grinned. "Says your smart."

"Yes, I met John in Doc's study group five years ago, we have a great deal in common. I just finished my last year of seminary and plan to start my own church." He found himself wanting to impress Joanne.

John said, "Couldn't help overhearing. Good decision."

Joanne said, "I'm majoring in business management and accounting. I want to work with a large corporation, possibly a megachurch. I've also talked to John a lot about his meetings with Doc. Did you know I met him a year ago? Fascinating man."

"What a big ambition," Allen said. "What do you do for fun?"

"Attend concerts. I can play a mean guitar when asked, which isn't often. I love music and dance."

"Tell me what you think of Doc's ideas?"

Joanne looked away for a second, then faced Allen. "I think he's close to the truth and I like a lot of what he says. Haven't studied his ideas in depth, but some seem dated, like not attractive to a lot of people. Is that important?"

"I'm dealing with the same problem. I've studied Doc's work in detail, could recite it all now from memory and I see the truth in what he postulates. But I look at today's world, the one where I'm starting a church, and I see people who want to feel better about themselves, not hear ministers proclaiming prophecy all the time."

He let his words fade into the distance. John said, "I'm not sure that's the best approach to bring new people into the church. We must live true to the word of God and His deeper intention to bring the Jews to know Jesus today."

"I know," Allen said. "the last book I want to water down is the Bible. I know how relevant it is to today's world. The world isn't ready to hear the message today. I need to go where I will reach them, not the other way around."

Joanne said, "I'm in the middle of this discussion. I'm no expert on the subject, but Doc's ideas, such as I know them, interest me. I agree it's hard to get people to listen to them today."

"Doc always said he would support me in any path I chose. I believe him."

"You letting Doc drive your decision?"

"He's moved on, but he's never pressured me. I trust God to guide me."

Alice said, "I've listened to this confusion for too long now. We need to get on with life." She finished the last of the fish on her plate. "Joanne, are you enjoying yourself tonight?"

"Of course. I like spirited discussions. Allen, I loved meeting you and I hope I'll see you around again." Allen intended to make such a meeting happen.

They finished dessert. John, Alice, and Joanne left. Allen sat at the table for a moment, listened to the clanking plates and crowd noise around him. What happened? Joanne intrigued him. Was it her willingness to state her own opinion, odd for such a young woman to already know what she wanted to do with her life? He played back the conversation again, respect for Doc, respect for his thoughts, likes music, dance, about his age and not started out in life yet. Yes, he liked her. A lot.

††††††††

How did two years pass so fast? Allen Rogers stood at the end of a row of five men in black tuxedos in a short corridor off to the side of the sanctuary. Wish Mom and Dad could be here for this big day, the celebration of his marriage to Joanne. Sadly, they both already went to be with the Lord. In front of him stood his best man, John Josephs.

So much happened in two years. He graduated seminary, found a small church to serve as assistant pastor for a year, courted Joanne from a distance while she finished college, and now today, in a small building in northern Illinois, the Senior Pastor of his new small Kingdom Today Center, a veterinary office turned church, 100 people sat in folding chairs while Doc stood at the lectern, ready to perform the ceremony. The band sat behind Doc, five pieces, including two guitars, drum set, saxophone, and a clarinet. Perfect for this new little church. He waited for the signal to enter the room.

They hadn't seen Doc in two years. Fortunately for Allen and Joanne, he called Allen out of the blue three months earlier, even though Allen had a new home address and phone number in a different state. When he heard Doc's voice he wondered, how did Doc find this information. Didn't matter.

"I'm glad to hear from you," Allen said. "I wanted to call you but couldn't find where you lived. Joanne and I are getting married, it will mean the world to us if you'd perform the ceremony."

"That's why I called," Doc said. "I'll be in your town the week of your wedding and I'd love to marry the two of you."

"Wonderful! I know Joanne will be happy."

He hung up the phone. How did Doc know about the wedding? How is it possible he's in our new town in Illinois the week of our wedding? Doesn't matter, he'll be here.

†††††††

Doc motioned to the head usher to lead the men into the sanctuary. In perfect silence all five men walked together to the right side of the stage. Allen walked to the center across from Doc, looked down the aisle at the closed door, waited. After a moment, the band started the wedding march, joyful music to watch his bride-to-be enter the sanctuary.

Flowers lined the aisle; each man wore a pink boutonniere. The door opened wide. A young girl in white dress with a basket in one hand walked in, scatted red rose petals along the aisle. Behind her came the bridesmaids, then the matron of honor, John's wife Alice, then the march music rose, the audience stood and in walked Joanne on the arm of her father, followed by her mother.

Allen watched the slow progression, the bridesmaids moved to the left side of the stage, held their bouquets in their hands, Joanne's mother sat in the front row.

Doc said, "We gather here today to celebrate the holy matrimony of Allen Rogers and Joanne Lewis. God brought Joanne and Allen together and blesses this union, which He made in Heaven and which will bless this world in the future." He turned to Joanne's father. "Who gives this woman to be married?"

"Her father and her mother," Mr. Lewis said.

Joanne stepped up beside Allen, Mr. Lewis sat beside his wife.

Doc said to John, "Do you have the rings?"

"Yes." He handed two small boxes to Doc.

Doc said, "Each of you wrote vows you wish to say at this time. I will hand each of you the ring you've chosen to symbolize your union together in God. After you say the vows, place the ring on your spouse's finger and say the words, 'With this ring I thee wed.'"

Doc handed one ring box to Joanne. She opened it, took out the ring, faced Allen, said, "I fell in love with you the day we met, and I will love you always. You are my soulmate, my guide, my mentor, my partner in life. I will serve you, advise you, be present for you, in every endeavor you undertake. I will raise our children in the Lord's ways. I will help you build this great church we stand in and help you to bring many people to Jesus Christ. I will walk with you hand in hand through this lifetime God granted us filled with love and support for you." She took his hand, slipped the ring onto his finger. "With this ring, I thee wed."

Doc handed the second ring box to Allen. He opened the box and put the ring into his right hand. "You came into my life a surprise, a gift from God through my best man John and his lovely wife Alice. You are an angel of God, the helpmate and companion I craved but never found for years. Together we will build this church, bring souls to Christ, make a difference for thousands of people. I cannot say what the future will bring. With God's guidance I will give you happiness, I will take care of you, love our children, love you with all my heart and soul. You are my soulmate, my confidante, my everything." He took her left hand, slipped the ring on her finger, said, "With this ring I thee wed."

Doc said, "You've both given your sacred vows before God and before this congregation. Under the authority of God the Father, Son and Holy Spirit, I pronounce you man and wife." He grinned. "Allen, you may kiss your bride."

He smiled at Joanne, took her in a strong embrace, kissed her with a passion he'd never known.

Doc said, "I present to you Pastor and Mrs. Allen Rogers!"

Allen and Joanne, hand in hand, walked down the aisle to a peppering of rice tossed from their close family and friends. The beginning of their new life, his ministry, with the woman he loved more than any other.

††††††

At the reception, after they cut the cake and tossed the garter and bouquet, Doc whispered in Allen's ear, "Can I speak with you a moment?"

Allen said, "Sure. In private?"

Doc led him into the side corridor.

"I hope you like what I've started to do here," Allen said. "This is my new church home and I'm going to build it into a powerhouse church and bring thousands to Christ."

"I believe you," Doc said. "You chose your path and I support you in any endeavor you pursue. Please remember to put God first in your efforts and keep in mind God's Holy Words of prophecy in the Bible, all of it. You'll be a wonderful Pastor. You're one of the students I'm most proud of, which is why I wanted to perform your wedding ceremony myself. Know God blessed you, trust He's assigned a guardian angel who'll always watch over you as you fulfill your destiny."

"Doc, I know how you feel about creating a church like this. I need to play down the God of judgement for a while to attract parishioners."

"I know. You will do what you need to do. I've given you a good grounding in prophetic end-times prediction theology. I appreciate your expertise and know you'll use what you know at the right time. For now, we part company. I leave you to your task here in Illinois."

Allen took Doc by the shoulders, gave him a big hug. "You've no idea how much you mean to me and to Joanne. We love you like a father. Be well."

Doc said, "Until we meet again."

He turned, walked up the aisle, out the door. Allen watched him disappear into the darkness, stood in the corridor for five minutes in joyous contemplation. He turned, walked back into the reception with its bright lights, loud music and celebrating friends and family. He belonged here.

Joanne found him five minutes later. "Hi, honey. I was looking for you. Where did you go?"

"Doc wanted to share a few ideas with me. I don't understand. I'm creating a church different from what he wants to see yet he told me to keep on with the good work. His predictions fascinate me. It's like I can't let go of them, like they follow me wherever I go. But deep in my heart, I feel prophecy teaching is not the way to build a church today. You're with me and John's with me. Together we can't fail."

Joanne said, "With God we can't fail. Do you sense He is with you?"

"Yes. Never a doubt in my mind. I'm on the right track."

"What about the predictions?"

"In good time I hope to expose the church to them. Not yet."

Joanne took his hand. "I care about you. You loved meeting with Doc all those years. What will happen without him? Sweetheart, I have an idea, you, John, Alice, and I love to study prophecies. I think a few others in the congregation share your views, at least in part, even if they don't know the background Doc gave you. Why don't the four of us meet next Thursday and see if we can't come up with a strategy for you to teach prophetic predictions to a small private weekly group?"

"I like your idea. Let's do it."

"You called me an angel tonight. I'm whispering in your ear like an angel does."

"I'm listening."

✝✝✝✝✝✝✝

Three days before the attack on Israel arrived, Allen and Joanne sat alone in their living room, waiting for the other members of their long-time Thursday night group meeting, which they dubbed Doc's Prophecy Club, to arrive.

"Can you believe it's almost thirty-five years since we last saw Doc at our wedding?" Joanne said.

"Where did that come from?" Allen asked.

"I've often wondered what happened to him," Joanne said. "He walked out of our wedding reception and vanished. Did you ever hear from him again?"

"No, nothing in all these years."

Allen thought for a moment. Darn it, why hadn't he attempted to see where Doc went? Was he trying to escape perceived restrictions on what he wanted to accomplish, and he'd accomplished a lot? Did he feel Doc might be disappointed? Allen's original thinking for forming a great church succeeded. His church, now 10,000 strong, dominated a small hillside in Illinois, the steeple and cross a beacon for miles around. People walked in the door, worshipped, became followers of Christ. Yet, something was missing, his messages felt weak, he wanted more. This couldn't be all there was.

"What are your thoughts and feelings at this moment?" Joanne asked.

"I don't know, I feel we've accomplished a lot, but I feel blah, as if I'm marking time. I don't know what else I can do. We built a great small group here on Thursday nights, but all we do is talk in private. I don't think my congregation wants full-throated prophetic predictions and preaching. Not even now as the world rebuilds after the Virus. I feel stuck. I'll continue to pray for God's guidance. It's hard to remain patient. I still pray for a major sign to get me out of this rut."

"Don't worry, honey," Joanne said. "You've taken the right path. God is showing you the way. Doc didn't try to talk you out of it."

"Doc didn't tell me to build this kind of church in so many words either, but he did say God would guide me. If He's guiding, I don't know where we're going. This morning I listed the fulfilled predictions Doc taught us years ago. I miss him. The prophecies came to me automatically, like I knew them so well they lost meaning. I don't even know any more if the possible final 12 events will happen in my lifetime, it's like a blur. Then I think: I attracted thousands of people to my congregation, a large television audience who loves what I teach and all we do is play good music and give them messages about how loving God is."

"They like the messages."

"I don't know what to share tonight in our small group. I'm going to let God guide me."

The doorbell rang. Allen answered. "Hi, John and Alice. I think Mike and Bill also planned to come tonight. That's our group."

John and Alice sat on the couch. The doorbell rang again. Mike, the local bank president, and Dr. Bill Wright, a surgeon at the local hospital, stood on the porch. "Come in, welcome," he said. "Eric, Todd and Sam couldn't join us tonight, so we'll go ahead without them. They all said they would be at church this coming Sunday."

The meeting started as usual, with refreshments in the kitchen. Joanne prepared a delicious casserole and dessert for everyone.

John tapped Allen on the shoulder. "What do you plan to talk about tonight?"

The words came from outside Allen's consciousness. "We haven't gone over the 12 fulfilled prophetic end-time predictions in a while. Maybe we'll do a review tonight to get them clear in our heads." I reviewed them this morning, so they are fresh on my mind.

"You seem tired lately. I don't see much of the old spark," John said with some concern.

"I built a big church with no idea what to do with it. We're growing in numbers but maybe not correctly for Jesus. People come and sing and listen and go home. It's like we've become a rock concert setting."

John said, "You don't challenge them much."

"How can I challenge thousands of people? I don't know most of them. They see me on the stage, the rock star preacher. They hear me on television then go back to their football games and forget what I said because it's the same old weak feel good message I've delivered for thirty-five years."

"What brought this on?"

"I don't know. Maybe I'm feeling my age, I don't feel a challenge anymore."

John ate one of Joanne's cookies. "These cookies taste great," he said. "Start talking when we gather in the living room. The right words will come."

Eventually the group moved into the living room and sat down, chatted.

Allen picked up the notes he'd prepared regarding the 12 fulfilled end-time prophecies earlier this morning. Maybe he could get out of this funk if he read them out loud to the group. He glanced through the pages. It all felt old, too familiar. Doc talked about them with passion, knew the details and yes, Allen knew the details too. What did he need with notes? He tossed the papers on the kitchen counter, strode into the living room. The conversation fell quiet, a surprising response among friends. He felt nudged to the center of the room. Usually he sat among the group, but tonight felt different, emboldened … confident. He stood in the center, faced them.

"Tonight, I'm going to go over the 12 fulfilled prophecies again in detail, give us all a solid sequence so we can remember them well. Sound good to everyone?"

Joanne looked surprised by the strength in his voice. Allen's countenance changed; she saw passion in his eyes she hadn't seen in years. John smiled and Alice perked up. Mike and Bill nodded yes.

"We know Doc's studies tell us God fulfilled twelve end-time signs, prophetic predictions made in the Bible, for us to see and 12 more are yet to arrive for us to see as well. One of the original twelve happened well after the last time we saw Doc, but I remember seeing it on his list as the 12th event, the abandonment of Gaza in 2005.[53]

"God is taking His time, but He does tell us once the final generational timeclock starts, with a generation being possibly 100 years,[54] this generation will not pass away until God completes His plans for mankind and specifically the Jews. Time is short. We believe the current generation, which started with the rebirth of Israel in 1948,[55] likely initiated a 100-year generational timeline. The last days began in 1914 and the fulfilled predictions show the Lord will return soon. We don't know when until we see the final 12 signs or prophetic predictions start to arrive. Let's go over the 12 fulfilled predictions tonight again and then talk about the thirteenth, which is one of great importance."

John said, "Let's review each one in order."

After they reviewed the prophecies the way Doc taught them, Allen said, "You can see how they fall into two major groups, those already fulfilled and those yet to come. The big one, and the next event, Prophecy 13, starts with an attack on Israel by surrounding enemy countries as explained in the books of Psalms and Ezekiel.[56] We

---

[53] Zephaniah 2:3-4

[54] Genesis 15:12-16, 400 years of Egyptian captivity, freed in the 4th generation, estimate 100-year generations.

[55] *Stunned*, 2015, Blomgren, pages 89-99

[56] Psalm 83, Ezekiel 38-39:16, war with a limited number of countries

don't know when this will happen, it will come without notice."

They discussed this prophecy in detail. "I love talking about these prophecies," Allen said. "The thirteenth is extremely important since it will inform us that the end is near and to get ready for the return of Jesus Christ."

Everybody said, "Amen."

"I'll see you all in church Sunday!" Allen said.

3

SERMON 1, PROPHECY 13

Allen stood at his podium, placed both hands on either side, looked out over the crowd. He felt exhilarated for the first time in years, as if a great weight lifted from his shoulders. Doc, seated directly in front of him in the first row, smiled, nodded his head as if he already knew what Allen planned to do. The crowd's murmurs faded into silent anticipation.

Allen prayed a quick silent prayer, *God, please guide me as I speak today to the thousands in your congregation and all over the world who gathered here today to hear your special message. Give me the words to express your will and plans today and every day into the future.* He paused, prepared to offer a new introductory prayer he had coincidentally created the night before and planned to use as his signature prayer today and before every service from this point forward. He spoke the words with a strong voice.

"Dear Lord, open our eyes today, that we may behold wonderful things out of your law. In Jesus' precious name, Amen.[57]

---

[57] Psalm 119:18

"Today I share with you a special message of reflection, hope, and wonder and, yes, make a major departure from my usual prepared message. For many years I've taught basic Gospel principles about the love of Christ and how this love can bring us to a close relationship with God.

"I have recently placed emphasis on God's comfort for mankind as the world struggles to rebuild after the Virus. I do not believe the Virus was a prophesied event, God did not cause the Virus to arrive, it was part of the nature of life on earth in the last days. As with all things, God, in His infinite wisdom, knew this would arrive in our time and may have greater significance for allowing the Virus to happen related to actual prophecies soon to arrive. I believe one large biblical prophecy arrived today; I will tell you shortly what I think occurred this morning and why.

"Let's first reflect on the Virus event a bit more as I believe it may have played an important role in resetting a world mindset for God's larger prophetic mission which is the second coming of His Son.

"Mankind in general had become arrogant and complacent.[58] People placed many gods in front of our true Lord. What gods might these be? Things like making jobs and careers more important than family, thinking that money, investments and the stock market offer safety and long-term security, idolizing celebrities and actors, movies, sports and sporting events, many of them occurring on Saturdays and Sundays, both intended as worship days. Air travel to resort destinations, hotels, gambling, alcohol, restaurants, bars, dance clubs, parties, all sorts of pampering spas and gyms were available at any

---

[58] Revelation 3:15-17

time. Essentially all *vanity of vanities* per the book of Ecclesiastes.[59] All these human pleasures tended to push God to the side due to possible superior attitudes. Many people arrogantly believed they were self-sufficient and had no need for God, as He tells us will happen in the last days in the book of Revelation.[60] Now, none of these things are necessarily bad in themselves when done in proportion and placing God first. Mankind had lost its true compass. With the Virus, everything we thought constituted a self-fulfilling pleasureful life, often devoid of God, came to a complete halt in mere days. Closing of businesses, restaurants, churches, sporting events, confined to our homes, separating from each other by government edict, edicts which God tells us to accept and follow without question[61] as He establishes all government authority. Even if you wanted to fight this, God says no, not wise.[62] Social distancing from all people, pondering our mortality, loneliness, anarchy caused by fear of not having food, supplies, medications, money, rent; world cities and streets deserted and empty leaving humanity restless and stir-crazy. What did this all do? It … humbled mankind! It left us all with a great deal of time to think about life, to recalibrate and ponder what is important in our lives, especially family and even God Himself. The world became a kinder place; most people treated strangers nicely and with respect as the true meaning of life became apparent. A worldwide saying took hold: "We are all in this together." God allowed the

---

[59] Ecclesiastes 1:2,14, 2:11,15,19,21,26, 4:4,7,8
[60] Revelation 3:17
[61] Romans 13:1-3, 1Peter 2:13-17
[62] Romans 13:1-3, 1Peter 2:13-17, follow edicts from government authorities.

hearts of the world to soften. We came to understand how weak, powerless, and small we really are in the whole scheme of life. How a single invisible microscopic organism had the power to bring mankind to its knees, the entire world came to a screeching halt. We experienced a great deal of time in quiet solitude for reflection.

"Now for the question many are asking, was this a natural occurrence or something manmade? The truth is in God's plans, it really doesn't matter as the Lord is in full control regardless of how this came to be, have no fear. I believe the effects the Virus has imparted on our societal mentality will become the larger story here. I believe it will play out in many intriguing ways within God's final 12 prophecies, all about to arrive. The first of the final twelve arrived this morning.

"Additionally, the Virus showed us how quickly the world population at large willingly surrendered personal freedoms with little protest. Even to the point of world governments requiring us all to put Apps on our phone so they can keep track of us regarding contagions. At first blush this sounds wise but the potential for less altruistic far-ranging implications is open ended. The powers of the world now know how easy it will be to control the masses in the future, just tell them anything that might frighten them into voluntary acquiescence. More than ever we must place our full trust in God alone.

"As another result of the Virus, the world printed so much fiat paper money that our economy and the whole world economy, in its current configuration, can never survive this. The economy has been decimated. Inflation has hit us hard. One amazing prophecy will soon arrive that may completely resolve the world financial crisis and put mankind at ease, but it will have consequences. All of this sets the table for God's final prophetic plans to arrive.

"Most important of all, the Virus caused a major diversion away from world events related to the Middle East and specifically Israel. While the world concentrated on China reparations for the Virus, nobody was watching what the enemy countries around Israel were planning. I will share with you shortly that what happened in Israel this morning was completely under the world's radar allowing an amazing major Biblical prophecy to arrive this very day. It was secretly easy to plan and implement, a fortuitous moment of opportunity for the enemies of Israel had arrived. Remember the word 'hook' which I will soon expound upon in my sermon today.

"Now, I did not share these things to scare you but to confirm and ultimately encourage you as we proceed. God knows exactly what is happening. If we follow Biblical prophecy, we are promised a good ending to what we are experiencing for those who trust Jesus.

"Over the next couple of years, as we see God's final last day plans unfold and we move into the future, I will share with you how the Virus changed the human mindset, opening the door for worldwide acceptance of some radical social, political and financial changes that under any other circumstances could not happen or would not be accepted. We will discover as prophecy unfolds that this will all be good news for Christians who know what is coming and why.

"When I built this church, I assumed modern day Christians didn't want to hear sermons based on Biblical prophecy, the Old Testament and Revelation. I've said many times from this stage these presumed dated ideas hold no relevance today, so every week I gave you my best feel-good sermons to bring you closer to Jesus Christ, or so I thought.

"I believed my task as a pastor for God's Kingdom was to teach these basic Gospel principles about the love of Christ, which meant I ignored significant truths and warning signs found in Old Testament prophecy.

He paused for a moment to let his words sink in.

"This morning, a few minutes before I started to speak, I finally understand a loving Father will always protect His children. He lovingly tells them in advance about future events. God did this through prophecy for centuries. One important verse in John is now my guide and compass, my anchor for future sermons. Please memorize this verse and take its words to heart:

John 14:29
29 *Now I have told you before it happens, so that when it happens, you may believe.*

"We don't always acknowledge God's deeper thoughts. Prior to the Virus we spent too much time on our daily lives, heads in the sand, ignoring warning signs God gave us as major blessings; being complacent. We let immediate gratification lifestyles consume us.[63]

He waited a moment, sensed discomfort in the congregation, heard the shuffle of feet and a low murmur of voices from within the hall.

---

[63] Luke 21:34-36

"I realized today I have not been fulfilling my responsibility to God. I apologized to Him for this error in judgment. I know through Christ He forgives me. Today I become a new man for God. With renewed passion I will teach the full truth with bold, honest passion for God's glory alone, beginning this morning. Today I desire to attempt to place the Virus in the rearview mirror because something spectacular started this morning. We will soon witness the most incredible set of events, designed by God, with the Jews in mind. I must share what I believe will come. God provides the proof. I proclaim His message. We are about to witness amazing events, EPIC beyond all comprehension.

"In the past, I've lightly preached God won't send any signs for us to literally see prior to the Lord's return, as God appears to tell us in Luke 17:20-21. Also, we cannot know the date or time of the Lord's return, a common teaching in most churches today... as fact. There may be an interesting twist to this thinking in the Bible and I will explain this in a future Major Sermon.

"Listen carefully. The current accepted traditional teachings are wrong! I knew for many years that God revealed 24 literal end-time prophecies in the Bible for us all to see. Twelve of these already happened and we have seen them.

Allen waited through a gasp of surprise. Once he said those words, he felt the Spirit of God fill his soul. He let the whispers die down, looked at Doc, at the enigmatic smile he flashed at him. No going back now.

"God specifically designed these 24 prophecies for us to witness. No, I'm not contradicting Luke. When you understand Luke's context, you will see what I mean. Pay no attention to the incorrect interpretation of Luke 17:20-21 to mean there will be no signs prior to the Lord's return. Jesus spoke to the Pharisees, the unbelievers in His day, in these verses. He tells them God will give no signs to 'unbelievers.' This means He reserved end-time signs for believers alone to see, as guided by the Holy Spirit, as blessings. The books of Joel and Luke[64] make this clear, last-day signs will occur to be witnessed by believers. Do not be deceived!

A few people in the back of the room stood and walked to the door. Allen looked around the auditorium. Everyone else sat in place, silent, waiting for his next words.

"This morning, before I came to church, I saw a sketchy news bulletin. Many of you may have seen the story as well. A major attack launched on Israel. I don't know the result. Another crisis in the Middle East. That's how conditioned I'd become.

"Then an extraordinary event happened. All of you saw it. After you settled into your seats, the back door opened, the center isle lit up and a man walked into the auditorium. I know most of you saw him but didn't know his identity. The arrival of this mystery visitor changed everything. With joy I acknowledge my oldest teacher and prophecy mentor, Doc, who sits in the front row today in a seat God reserved for him.

"I last saw him 35 years ago. He taught me all I know about Biblical prophecy, my secret passion and hobby for the past 42 years. Why did Doc step into this hall after a

---

[64] Joel 2:30-31, Luke 21:25-28

35-year separation? I believe he arrived today to make me feel at peace with what I share with you today. I believe God knew about this day and guided me through Doc to proclaim His truth. I didn't plan the message I share today. God planted it within me moments ago through His infinite wisdom.

"This morning I learned the staff lost last week's TV sermon, which normally airs today. We cannot air it this morning. For those in my television audience, you're hearing this message live today in real time." He paused for a few seconds, then smiled. "Seems like a lot of coincidences for this specific day, don't you think? No coincidence exists when God gets involved.

"I mentioned earlier how God fulfilled twelve of His 24 end-time prophecies already. I will go over them in more detail shortly.

"A major prophecy arrived this morning and woke me from my spiritual slumber. I believe the attack on Israel this morning is the Thirteenth Event in God's end-time set of prophetic signs for us to witness. It's a big one. Among the 24 end-time events are three super signs, prominent ones we can all see with significant importance. The first was the founding of Israel in 1948. The attack this morning is the second.

"Our lives are about to change in incredibly exciting ways. I believe in the next week we will discover the event this morning will be God's two-minute warning for mankind, showing us the Lord is about to return; not secretly but in a more spectacular way than the church today ever thought possible."

"I feel the Holy Spirit compelled me today. I'm not going out on a limb with what I'm about to share. I know these ideas are new to you. Bear with me with an open mind. You're probably wondering what these mysterious twelve completed prophecies cover, what they say, and how we know they already happened. After I explain the first twelve events, I'll deal with the attack on Israel this morning. which again I believe arrived today. Here are God's twelve incredible fulfilled end-time prophecies we've seen.

"God designed all 24 prophetic end-time events as signs for 'believers' to witness in the last days. God gave us these signs as blessings for Christians and Jews, to offer us both proof and comfort. They are the greatest of all blessings for His Glory alone. But what is His Glory? The answer comes from the book of Isaiah 46:12, where God says, *'Israel is His Glory,'* then in Isaiah 48:11 He says, *'My Glory I will not give to another.'* This *'will not give to another'* means never, for all time, so Christians never replaced the Jews, even to this day.

"As with God's John 14:29 verse, He says in Mark 13:23 'He tells us everything in advance.' We've arrived at the time for the final twelve of God's prophesied end-time signs to appear. Twelve already happened and we witnessed them.

"I believe God intended to use all 24 prophecies to indicate in a visual way when Christ will return to take His believers, His bride, home with Him to His heavenly Kingdom, a two-stage return stretched over seven years. I will provide strong Biblical support for this seven-year two-stage return concept in coming sermons. The final 12 events, when completed, will give us a high level of certainty this version of events is true. Before the thirteenth event this morning in Israel, I was weak. Deep inside I remained skeptical about what I'd share with you today and in coming years. Today's events changed me, set me on a new amazing course for Jesus. We are blessed to soon see the grandeur of God's end-time plans unfold. Some events will challenge us but if we know what they mean and what He does and why, we can experience joy, not trepidation. To be clear, do not think what occurred this morning is the beginning of WWIII, or Armageddon as this cannot be true per a set of verses in Revelation[65] and Luke.[66] A war will not destroy the United States or our world at this time, but our country will drastically change soon by God's design. I will address how and why this will occur in a future Major Sermon. In fact, in Luke[67] we learn the world will remain at peace until one specific day at the Lord's initial return within the final 24th prophecy. I will also address this spectacular event in a coming Major Sermon. I will now explain God's 12 previously fulfilled end time prophecies.

"The first and second prophecies in God's list of twenty-four represent two events that began in 1914 related to God's Glory, Israel. God refers to them in the Bible as two birth pangs to look for.[68] The first prepared

---

[65] Armageddon, Revelation 16-18, happens close to the end of the last half of the Tribulation.

[66] Luke 17:26-36, Peace in time of Noah before flood, Lot before Sodom's destruction, so will it be in the days of the Son of man. *Stunned*, 2015, Blomgren, pages 205-209

[67] Luke 17:27-30

[68] Matthew 24:4-8

the land of Israel for the Jews, and the second the Jews for the land.

"The two events, World War I and World War II, created a break with the past 1,900 years, when the Jews were scattered by God to all corners of the earth after the destruction of the second Temple in 70 AD. World War I and World War II started the Jews on their way back to their originally promised homeland. Most of God's prophecies deal with His ongoing, never ending relationship with the Jews. We forgot or discounted how Israel plays a role of supreme importance in all end-time prophecy. The wars, the birth pangs, indicate we live in the season of the return of Jesus.

"After World War I, the old Ottoman Empire, which controlled the Middle East and the ancient land of Israel, collapsed. The British took control of the Holy Land after the war. When the war ended, Great Britain decided to honor a Jewish scientist, Dr. Chaim Weizmann,[69] who played a critical role in helping them win the war. They asked him what they could do to reward him. He said he wished for the land of Israel to be declared as a possible rejuvenated future homeland for his people. Soon thereafter, in 1917, Great Britain issued the Balfour Declaration, which declared the area of current-day Israel as a possible new revived homeland for the Jewish people. The land was now ready for the people, but the people weren't ready for the land … yet.

"In WWII, Adolf Hitler, through one of his henchmen, Karl Adolf Eichmann,[70] carried out the holocaust. By the

---

[69] *Stunned*, 2015, Blomgren, page 93
[70] *Stunned*, 2015, Blomgren, page 94

end of the war, half of all the Jews in the world were exterminated. The remaining Jews feared for their lives. Most didn't want to stay in alien societies any longer. If God hadn't scattered them all over the world, they could have been annihilated.

"God knows what he's doing. The result, at the end of the war in mid-1945, the Jewish people became ready for the land.[71]

"The third event comes from Luke.[72] At the end of the war, to prevent future conflicts like the two world wars, all world governments formed the United Nations in San Francisco in October 1945. For the first time an international body could guide all nations to mutual decisions. This organization will play a pivotal role in many of the remaining prophetic events, good and not so good. No World War III will be seen while Christians are still on earth. I will provide proof in a later Major Sermon. Instead, the world will enter a false peace until the Lord returns at a specific moment, as we learn also in Luke.[73]

"With this new United Nations formed, the fourth event centered around the formal world recognition and ratification of the new State of Israel in one day[74] on May 14, 1948, the first of three major super signs on God's twenty-four-event end-times Road Map. This became the major good prophetic event that came out of the United Nations; everything else goes downhill from there.

---

[71] *Stunned,* 2015, Blomgren, page 94
[72] Luke 21:29-32, *Stunned,* 2015, Blomgren, pages34 and 94-95. The fig tree and all the trees.
[73] Luke 17:26-41
[74] Isaiah 66:7-8

"This rebirth of the State of Israel officially started the final generational timeclock of the last days.[75] A generation can be defined as 100 years per a reading in Genesis 15.[76] In Matthew[77] the Bible indicates "this final generation will not pass away until all these events take place." Based on the birth of Israel, God intended for us to recognize this as His Biblical final generation, which again could span up to 100 years.

"How might we know Israel plays the key role to start the end-times generation? God shows us in an incredible way. Let's assume for a moment the State of Israel is a living person. Look at Israel as a Jewish man, growing from an infant into manhood. In Isaiah,[78] God shares about a future birth or rebirth ... this relates to Israel today. In Isaiah we hear about the birth of a 'man child' (Greek 'genea' = born one) and a 'land born in one day.' We've witnessed this. Based on the life cycles of a Jewish human male, amazing historical events and timing occurred since Israel's May 14, 1948 rebirth.[79]

"The rebirth of the State of Israel started a generational time clock. It started a literal timeline all Christians who love the study of end-time prophecies must understand. God graciously provided additional indications to validate this and they are all amazing!

"Symbolically, on May 14, 1948, the date of Israel's rebirth, many surrounding enemy Arab countries became

---

[75] Matthew 24:34, Luke 21:3, *Stunned*, 2015, Blomgren pages 95-96

[76] Genesis 15:12-16, 400 years Egyptian captivity, freed in the 4th generation so we can infer a generation is 100 years.

[77] Matthew 24:34

[78] Isaiah 66:7-8

[79] These events are all true in the real world today.

irritated. They decided to fight against Israel on day one of the new country's existence and said they would take it down quickly. All their efforts failed. This irritating action symbolically relates to a Jewish boy's circumcision.

"A Jewish boy becomes responsible for his actions, accountable, at 13 years of age. He becomes a Bar Mitzvah. The Jewish people hold a Bar Mitzvah ceremony for the young man to celebrate this milestone. In World War II, remember the German I mentioned earlier, Karl Adolf Eichmann. He acted as the chief architect of the Holocaust. He escaped at the end of the war and remained a fugitive until his capture by the Israelis in 1960. On December 15, 1961, an Israeli court convicted him and held him 'accountable' for the deaths of millions of Jews. Israel was thirteen years and seven months old when this happened. Israel celebrated this event.

"A Jewish man becomes eligible to fight in wars while in his 20th year of life (after his 19th birthday). Adding 19 years to 5-14-1948, we get 5-14-1967. On 6-7-1967 (Israel was 19 years and 23 days old), Israel fought and won the Six-Day War, and the City of Jerusalem returned to the control of the Jewish people . . . after more than 1,900 years in exile—a fulfillment of prophecy.[80]

"Symbolically, in the life of a Jewish man, he becomes a man of peace at the age of 30. Jesus, our Rabbi Messiah, started His formal ministry at 30 years of age. Thirty years added to 5-14-1948 equals 5-14-1978. In September 1978, when Israel was 30 years and 4 months old, it negotiated the Camp David Peace Accords. Then, in March 1979 (Israel was 30 years and 10 months old), Egypt and Israel,

---

[80] Luke 21:24, Jerusalem no longer trampled under the foot of the Gentiles

brokered by Jimmy Carter, signed the Camp David Peace (security) Accords. This plan made it possible to keep the borders with Israel and its neighbors safe by agreement — another fulfillment of prophecy.

"Israel will turn 100 years of age in May 14, 2048, so this is likely our remaining 'season' for God's 24 events to take place and reach fulfillment.

"We are directed in the book of Luke to stay aware of what goes on in our world and to correctly analyze the present time in which we live.[81]

"Is it possible these events are random chance? No! God shows us how the rebirth of the State of Israel officially started the final Biblical prophetic generational timeclock.

"The fifth event occurred and is ongoing today. Once Israel existed, they proclaimed a right of return, welcomed all Jews to emigrate to Israel by virtue of their birth heritage and religion. Thousands of people left their old unsafe home countries of origin and migrated to the new land of Israel as predicted in Ezekiel, Zephaniah, and Jeremiah.[82] People flooded into their new homeland country.

"The sixth event, the capture of Jerusalem in 1967, happened years later. After 1900 years of Jewish exile, Jerusalem came under full Jewish control, fulfilling the ending of the time of Gentiles predicted in Luke.[83]

"The next four prophetic events, seven through ten, deal with the world at large and cover major social trends

---

[81] Luke 12:54-56, emphasis on verse 56
[82] Ezekiel 37:11-14, Zephaniah 2:1-2, Jeremiah 31:8
[83] Luke 21:24

we've seen since the end of World War II. Technology developed during World War II set off most of these developments but tensions inside the Catholic Church set off others. A new world emerged, yet God knew what must transpire.

"Christianity faced challenges almost from the beginning two thousand years ago. Controversy raged inside the early church until the split within Eastern Orthodox Churches in 1054 over long-standing issues. We don't need to go into the theology involved at this time. We also went through the Reformation in the 1500's which split Protestantism off from Catholicism.

"Then came the French Revolution, when the French introduced the idea of secularism and the Americans introduced the idea many different religions could coexist. No single established church was needed. For the first time, people could live without religion and many did. The Great Age of Apostacy accelerated and grows like a cancer today. Most people fell away from the true church of God and many publicly proclaimed Christians believe false doctrines. This falling away, or apostasy, is the seventh event, predicted to arrive in the last days in Thessalonians and both letters of Timothy.[84]

"We are aware of the eighth event today. Daniel[85] predicted a key social trend set to happen exponentially in the last days, the increase and ease in travel, especially consider jet travel going back and forth, the rise of computers, and the massive increase in knowledge. Everyone who owns a smart phone today possesses a

---

[84] 2 Thessalonians 2:1-3, 1 Timothy 4:1, 2 Timothy 4:3-4, Hebrews 5:11-14
[85] Daniel 12:4

wealth of knowledge in the palm of their hands; unthinkable and unimaginable when the book of Daniel was written.

"Number nine is prophesied in Psalms 83.[86] We've lived with this one for centuries, but it's become much more rabid lately, with the holocaust of Hitler and hatred for the State of Israel and the Jews among many millions of people. Anti-Semitism was always with us, but the Jews managed to coexist with Gentile societies for centuries. Many nations want Israel wiped off the face of the earth so Israel will be remembered no more.[87] Anti-Semitism is now worse than ever, as prophesied.

"Number ten is small but mighty and relates to the possible Mark of the Beast technology available today as mentioned in Revelation.[88] Technology arose so rapidly and gave governments so much possible control over our lives with cell phones and computer chips, Facebook and Twitter, DNA, all tools a corrupt leader could coopt, allowing him to monitor where you are at all times, and take control of your health care, finances and spending habits. This technology exists today and, as we have seen after the Virus, is being highly utilized today.

"The eleventh event or prediction tells us we will know the return of the Lord is close when Israel lives securely in unwalled villages and cities, inside their country per Ezekiel.[89] First, Israel needed to exist for this to occur, which happened in 1948. The villages inside Israel today are unwalled, as predicted, though the country built an

---

[86] Psalm 83:1-4
[87] Psalm 83:3-4
[88] Revelation 13:15-18
[89] Ezekiel 38:8, 11, 14

exterior perimeter border wall, a significant distinction. The land of Israel lives in peace inside its own boundaries including Jews, Arabs, and Christians.

"Finally, for the twelfth event, from Zephaniah[90] we are told how, in the last days, the Jews would abandon Gaza. This event occurred recently when Israel, in search of peace, gave Gaza to the Arabs in 2005. This was a failure.

"God through prophecies made a strong point: all twenty-four predictions need to happen for mankind to witness before Jesus Christ the Lord returns. The twenty-fourth will be so spectacular it will change the trajectory of mankind in unbelievable ways. I will share more on this set of events in prophecy 24, which will be epic, in future Major Sermon #5.

"God gave us the ability to see all the signs of His Son's return. Remember again Mark and John[91] tell us God shows us everything in advance so when we see events we will believe. God shows us 24 major end-time signs. As I have now explained, we've clearly seen twelve of them fulfilled as God shared out of His Bible.

"What I share with you today raises problems for many Christians and is one reason many don't accept God's prophecies or signs these days. Luke does appear to say God will give no signs prior to the return of Christ. Yet, as I mentioned earlier and emphasize now, when we look closer at the context, it becomes clear unbelievers will not see the signs, only believers should see them. God gave them to us so we will know how to cope with a drastically changing world. God doesn't desire to leave us frightened

---

[90] Zephaniah 2:3-4
[91] Mark 13:23, John 14:29

and in the dark, we are to be in the light, we are His children, He cares for us. The signs issue creates huge problems for contemporary churches, ours included. I never preached that we won't see signs, but I neglected to emphasize that we as believers are to see all God's signs.

"It's interesting that at my weekly prophecy class, where I meet Thursday nights with a small group of friends, we reviewed all the twelve prophecies I just shared with you only three days ago. How profound in retrospect. Coincidence? We also went over the thirteenth prophecy in detail. I didn't need notes then or today. I mentioned to the group I didn't see any indicators of this big 13th event happening any time soon.

"Then all the events early this morning and at our service fell in place as if God planned it. I believe God was the choreographer. However, was the attack on Israel this morning the event described in Psalm 83 and Ezekiel 38?[92] I believe it was and will ask you to do one thing this week. Watch and listen to what events transpire and see if what I'm about to tell you describes the event accurately. If I'm correct based solely on Bible prophecy, not my own wisdom, we may discover what I'm about to tell you matches Bible prophecy and today we witnessed the arrival of God's thirteenth event, our two-minute warning that Christ is about to return.

"Now let's turn to the future, to this next week to be specific, when I believe we will see certain events happen in the areas around Israel for specific reasons which I will now share with you. If I'm correct, we will see confirmation this week.

---

[92] Psalm 83, Ezekiel 38-39:16

"To understand today's conflict, related to Israel, and why it is so important to God's plan, we need to look back almost four thousand years, to Abraham, who Jews and Christians together and Islam separately claim as their patriarch. The Islamic side of the family claims Abraham's first son Ishmael, born of his wife's maidservant at his wife's behest, as Abraham's rightful heir. The Judaic/Christian side of the family claims his second son Isaac, born of his wife Sarah 13 years later, in her old age, as the rightful heir. The feud over who is the correct heir and who should rule the land of Israel continues to this day.

"From the Judaic/Christian side of the argument, the issue was settled when the Old Testament book of Genesis was completed around 1,450 BC.[93] Genesis tells us Isaac is the true heir.

"From the Islamic side, the Koran, the Holy book of Islam, completed in 632 AD, says Ishmael is the true heir.

"They can't both be right. A critical note: the book of Genesis was completed over 2,000 years before the Koran. God says His Bible is perfect.[94] Followers of Islam claim the Koran is perfect.

"Both the Bible and the Koran tell us a conflict will take place in Israel between the currently feuding two families of Abraham. This event will decide which side of the family will prevail. As with any conflagration, there can only be one victor ... that's life. I believe this battle occurred today and we will learn this week which side prevailed.

---

[93] Genesis 17:21, 21:1-8, 22:9-18
[94] Hebrews 4:12-13, 6:18, 2 Timothy 3:16-17, 2 Peter 1:20-21, Revelation 1:3

"I imagine all of you are asking a simple question: 'Why now?'

"The simple answer is: God chose this time. A more complex answer brings into play today's geopolitical situation and economic realities in the Middle East. We know for years now, many Islamic countries around Israel attempted to create a coalition to plan how to attack and rid the world of the Jewish people as shown in Psalm 83.[95] Prior to today, since the formation of Israel in 1948, these primarily Arabic and Persian nations based their historical hatred for the Jews on the belief they were invaders in the land of Israel.

"This dynamic severely shifted when an Israeli-based oil company announced it discovered the greatest natural gas and oil fields in the world in the Golan Heights,[96] which positions them to become one of the greatest exporters of these products and makes Israel a deadlier threat to the economic balance of the region. Israel can get these products to market quickly and could easily flood the market in the region with cheap efficient energy. The economies of Russia and the Arabs can't compete as there will be enough gas and oil from Israel alone to destroy their economies. This cannot be allowed to happen so they planned to take this gas and oil referred to in the Bible as plunder[97] from Israel by force in a surprise attack[98] they believed would destroy the State of Israel and its small band of Jews. They see 200,000,000 Arabs against 8,000,000

---

[95] Psalm 83:1-4
[96] This actually happened in the real world recently.
[97] Ezekiel 38:12-13
[98] Ezekiel 38:11-12

Jews, an enticing hook,[99] and believe there is no human way they could lose with such overwhelming numbers. Human is the key word here; God can do anything, and He will. I believe He did today.[100]

"This discovery led to attempts to form a larger, more diverse coalition to attack Israel now led by Russia to the North, along with Syria and Turkey. This coalition also includes many of Israel's surrounding Arab neighbors, including Egypt and other northeastern African countries, certain western European countries, significantly Germany, and from the east, Jordan, Iraq, Iran, and Saudi Arabia.

"These dynamics, together with the new oil and gas fields, infuriated both the Arabs and the coalition to a point of frenzy. They believe this wealth belongs to them, not the Jewish invaders. All these factors plant multiple hooks, or enticements, by the hand of God in the jaws of the coalition,[101] and this plunder[102] changes the dynamics of what is happening around Israel. A serious conflict became inevitable. This was not really intended to be a human war but a God war. [103]

"Why is Russia so important? For the last couple of decades, Russia, directly north of Israel,[104] became a main player with the Arabs in the Middle East and created a vast military presence in the region near the Israeli border in

---

[99] Ezekiel 38:4
[100] Ezekiel 39:1-8
[101] Ezekiel 38:4 note hooks is plural, there will be more than one
[102] Ezekiel 38: 11-13, Ezekiel 39:10
[103] Ezekiel 39:1-7
[104] Ezekiel 38:6

Syria.[105] I believe Magog in the Bible,[106] specifically noted as part of this Prophecy 13 war, is Russia, with Gog its leader. Half of the Russian army today is Islamic.[107] Russia's main export is the sale of natural gas and oil to this entire region. These products are the main money makers for all the Arab nations surrounding Israel as well. Without these sales they would be financially decimated.

"The Bible makes clear these events are about to happen. Prophecy 13, the second major super sign of the return of Jesus Christ to Earth as explained in Ezekiel, has arrived. The situation in the Middle East today changed radically. The Russian/Arab alliance formed because both wanted Israel to vanish from the earth. They believe Ishmael to be Abraham's true heir and Isaac, who represents Israel, to be a usurper of the rights of Ishmael who was firstborn. Isaac is an inferior invader who must be destroyed. The Arabs and Russia justified this plan to destroy Israel by saying they desire to take plunder per the book of Ezekiel from inside Israel.[108] All their claims are wrong. This week God will miraculously resolve this feud in Israel's favor. All Arab claims since 1948 in the family feud that Israel is the problem as explained in Psalm 83 [109] will be shattered.

"We will see massive destruction and major loss of life in all the coalition countries I mentioned. No human army is responsible. This will be a pure Act of God. Others will

---

[105] This is true today in the real world today.

[106] Ezekiel 38:1-3, 15 also remotest northern land Ezekiel 38:6 is Russia today. Moscow it directly to the north of Israel today.

[107] This is true in the real world today.

[108] Ezekiel 38:12-13

[109] Psalm 83, Psalm 83:13-18, *Stunned*, 2015, Blomgren, page 124

dismiss this claim, but we know God[110] made these events happen, and resolved them, on a grand scale.

"Again, the Bible explicitly says God will put hooks in their jaws[111] to bring these enemies against Israel. These items I showed you are all big hooks.

"When the surprise attack occurred, and look specifically for this, God turned their weapons of war back on them by divine intervention, leading to the selective destruction of the Radical factions of Islam. Prophecy 13, as described in Psalm 83 and Ezekiel 38, is this morning's reality. Israel could do absolutely nothing. The attack caught them off guard. They expected to be overwhelmed. God will have won this war for Israel all by Himself.

"Watch for all these events predicted in the Bible. Satellite photos will reveal the current land of Israel escaped virtually unharmed. The land to the east and north up to the Euphrates River will also be virtually unharmed but many people will have died mysteriously. The land to the south and west to the Rivers of Egypt is also unharmed but many will be dead there as well.

"In Jerusalem, the Dome of the Rock will be flattened. The same fate will befall Medina and Mecca in Saudi Arabia, but why?[112] The destruction will seem almost surgical.

"One major religion will be decimated. The God of Abraham, Isaac and Jacob will prevail with no help from mankind. The god of Abraham and Ishmael will not.

---

[110] Psalm 83:13-18

[111] Ezekiel 38:4, hooks, represent God prompting the enemy to come against Israel

[112] The Jews need to build their new Temple on the site currently occupied by the dome of the rock. This will be addressed in our story in Major Sermon #3.

"Watch this week to see if all this occurred. If yes, we will have visual confirmation that the God of Abraham, Isaac, and Jacob is at work. I believe the Bible shares these events with us and the result is incredible.

"We have all been struggling with the rebuilding process after the Virus dissipated. We must understand that we will soon learn that the Virus event may pale in comparison to what God started today. As prophecies unfold, we will discover God's true plan for the Virus and how it will all play out for the good in God's master plan for His Glory Israel. Everything is by design.

"In closing, I always loved prophecy but didn't know when to share it. With the attack on Israel this morning, I know the time is now. Everything points to this being the mission God prepared me for during my 60 years of life. God gave me this platform, this church. It's not my own doing. Our church in Illinois exists today because of the support of family and friends and most important of all our Savior Jesus Christ.

"I believe God guided each of you in attendance today and on television to this ministry for a greater purpose. Nothing happens by chance. Please pray deeply this week for God to show you what He has planned for you at this pivotal moment in history. All we can collectively do is watch the signs, prepare ourselves as best we can, and trust fully in our magnificent Lord.

"I hope what I shared with you today along with the events we will look for this week in the news will give you serious room for thinking that what I shared about the possible outcome of the Israel attack this morning will prove accurate this week. If yes, come back or tune in next week as I will address the next four prophetic events, numbers fourteen to seventeen, that will rapidly occur almost simultaneously. You will need to know what to look for and how to prepare. All these events will give Glory to God and peace for all of us.

"Now in the name of the Father, Son and Holy Spirt may you have peace and joy as we leave today. We give thanks to the God of Abraham, Isaac, and Jacob for all the blessings we are receiving in the fulfillment of your end-time prophecies. We pray this in the divine name of Jesus the Christ. May God be with you all this week, Amen."

The crowd sprang to their feet and gave the pastor a rousing two-minute raucous standing ovation, one like he never heard before. Almost like God was pleased.

Doc smiled. ☺

4

PROPHECY 13 IS VERIFIED

After the sermon, John walked briskly towards Allen at his podium from the off-stage area. "Come on," he said. "You can't talk to everyone. We need to get off stage before the crowd mobs you."

Allen saw the aisles swell with thousands of people excited by what they heard heading towards the stage. John's right, chaos was about to erupt, better to let the professionals handle the crowd.

He followed John off stage, around a corner, up a staircase, into the private office he used to view the audience before he gave his sermon every week.

"Can we get the news here?" he asked, then realized he knew the answer, cable feeds are in the television studio next door.

The oddity of the situation jarred him. Why wasn't John surprised at what he'd done?

John said, "Of course." He followed John to the TV studio. John glanced back at him, smiled, opened the door. "Ready for you right now. Joanne will arrive in a few minutes."

"You're a mind reader," Allen said.

"Not quite. A sign of how well I know you after all these years."

Joanne walked in. "You were wonderful at the pulpit."

†††✡†††

John turned on the television system, found a live news show, difficult on a Sunday morning. A reporter based in Tel Aviv, Israel reported, "...heard from the Prime Minister's office a few minutes ago. They said they heard the early reports as well but denied any damage or any sign of armies or missiles at all. This is strange because our correspondent in Amman reported massive army movements towards the Israeli border earlier this morning."

Allen listened. Was this a dud, a false report? Did he go out on a limb for nothing? Of course not, he reminded himself. He spoke as guided by the Holy Spirit which is never wrong.

The reporter continued, "Back to you in Washington."

An anchorman came on the air, "This is strange, we've heard no major reports of damage in Israel as well. Let's bring in our correspondent in Tehran for another perspective." He paused a moment. "What do you mean you can't get through? Keep trying." He turned back to the camera. "We're working to get confirmation from the region and will be back when we get more updates for you."

The news went off, a sporting event came on.

Allen stared at the television screen, then turned to John. "What do you think?"

"I think you're an incredible pastor with the most important message in the world right now. Let's get lunch, go home, and wait for the networks to catch up with God. Right now, it's all second hand, no eyewitness reports."

Joanne said, "You presented the message everyone needed to hear, and you told them to watch the news for the next few days for confirmation. It's early."

The door to the television room opened. Doc walked in.

Allen stared a moment, then said, "I'm sorry I never called."

"You wouldn't get through," Doc said. "I've worked on a special assignment for a while. Allen, you did a masterful job today and you'll do another one next Sunday, when all becomes clearer to the whole world. Don't despair. You have it right, trust God, trust your own ability, and watch the news. This will take a few days to play out. By next Sunday, you'll know exactly what to say."

"You seem to know things I don't."

"Rest assured you know as much as I do," Doc said. "You don't realize it yet."

"Can you come back to the house and visit with us for a while?" Joanne asked.

"Joanne, Allen, John, I wish I could. You already know what's about to happen. The world will see it in the next day or two." He smiled. "It's spectacular! I've got another engagement abroad so I will need to take leave of you. Know I love all of you and will always be there for you. Your work is God's work. Never forget that."

He stepped back, turned, walked towards the door.

John called out, "Doc, when will you get back here?"

"I'll see you soon." Doc walked out the door, which closed behind him with a click.

Allen listened for footsteps but heard none. Doc, he thought, I hope you know what you're doing. He shook his head. No, Doc is special. He knows.

†††✡†††

The afternoon and evening's news added little more information than Allen heard Sunday morning. He stood to turn the television off at midnight when the newscaster broke in, "We received a message from our correspondent in Jerusalem and we're setting up a live feed right now. He's ready with an astounding report for us."

Allen stood still, watched with fascination. A few minutes passed, then the camera showed the early sunrise over Jerusalem and a young reporter standing on the roof of a building with the cityscape in the background. Allen tried to identify the area, which looked familiar but odd at the same time. He couldn't figure it out.

The correspondent said, "Zev Katz reporting from Jerusalem. We finally received definitive word from the government regarding yesterday's events. I say events because although we found a lot of debris scattered around the country, Israel experienced no severe damage to its cities and towns, no damage at all. Except in one place and it's inexplicable. Behind me is the Temple Mount. You might usually see the Dome of the Rock, the holiest Muslim shrine in Israel, with its Golden Dome. It's gone, destroyed, leveled to the ground. The strangest part, nothing else around the Temple Mount site is touched, none of the Israeli establishments nor the Wailing Wall, all intact. I repeat, the Dome of the Rock and all other Muslim sites on the Temple Mount are destroyed. Israel was not touched.

"I also talked to the Israeli deputy prime minister an hour ago. He told me the first notice of the attack hit Sunday afternoon here, Sunday morning in the United States, and completely surprised them, the IDF was not mobilized or on alert. Nothing. He said he heard rumors of millions of men marching towards Israel from all sides and called the Prime Minister and Cabinet together. They ordered IDF mobilization, it was too late. We waited for disaster to strike.

"Nothing happened. It's odd, crazy. The Arabs totally outnumbered us. Where are they? No Israelis died, no armies appear to have crossed our borders, missiles heading toward us vanished off the radar. The attack, whatever it was, started as an event of Biblical proportions and then ... ended. I'll be back with another report as soon as more news is available."

The picture switched back to the news anchor in the newsroom. "We've tried to reach our reporters in Iran and Saudi Arabia, but nobody responds. We'll be back on the air once we make contact."

Allen turned the television off. He held Joanne in his arms. "Honey, it's started," he said. They stared at the empty screen, each alone with their thoughts. After a few minutes, they quietly rose and went to bed.

Early Monday morning, Allen went to his church office to ponder the previous day's events. He turned on the television on the office wall, tuned it to the news. Nothing different from the day before, lots from Israel, mostly about the destroyed weapons scattered around the country in mounds everywhere; incredibly they did no harm. The biggest question became how these weapons failed so completely without any defensive weapons fired in return?

Allen figured he knew the answer. God.

A knock on the door startled him.

"Come in," he said.

His assistant walked in, an envelope in her hand. "This came for you." She handed the envelope to him.

He turned it over. Registered mail from Paris, France. Sent yesterday? How could it get here the next day in the morning if mailed on a Sunday? Who could make that happen? The idea intrigued him. It even had no return address. He hesitated a moment. What if it contained dangerous contents? One couldn't be too careful with mail these days. Instinct, was it God? He felt a sense of peace, opened the letter. The envelope contained one folded sheet of paper. He unfolded it, read.

"Dear Pastor Rogers,

"I listened to your sermon Sunday afternoon, France time, and am intrigued by your ideas. I plan to pay more attention to your sermons in coming weeks.

"You know nothing about me. My name is Guy Terrestre. I'm a financial advisor based here in Paris and was recently named to the Board of Directors of the World

Bank, representing France. My family owns a large bank here in Europe of which I'm managing partner.

"You are probably wondering why I took an interest in you.

"It's simple. Your ideas fascinate me, and I want to know more about them. I'm keeping a sharp eye on what you're doing since I also may work in the religious arena in the future.

"My Best Wishes,

"Guy Terrestre"

Allen stared at the letter for a while. What might this man want from a country preacher in America? Why from Paris? He bears watching.

His office door opened. Doc walked in, sat in the chair in front of his desk.

"What a surprise," Allen said, "I thought you went off on business abroad?

"I was, I made a quick trip to Paris for an early morning meeting."

"Illinois?"

"France."

Allen stared at him. France? Since Sunday … yesterday? He did a quick calculation, only hours to get there and back? "Too quick."

"While I was there, I ran into an interesting man, by the name of Guy Terrestre. Don't know if you ever heard of him."

Allen leaned toward him. "Please, sit down, Doc." He picked up the letter. "I received a letter this morning by registered mail." He handed it to Doc.

"The same person?" he said.

Doc read the letter twice, handed it back to Allen. "I'm not surprised," he said.

Allen said, "I know nothing about him but what's in this letter. You said you met him."

Doc sat back in his chair as deciding what to say. Allen waited.

"Here's what I know," Doc said. "I spent two full hours with him in Paris over brunch, right after he joined the World Bank board. He told me the whole story about how he got the appointment. Seems his family runs high in Paris banking circles and his parents are good friends with the president of France, who appoints the French board members. He graduated from the Ecole Militaire in Paris, served as an officer in the French army for two years. He is now a charismatic public speaker and advocate for strong government in France."

"Why show an interest in me?"

"He didn't mention you when we talked." Doc pulled out his cell phone. "Here's his picture."

Allen looked into the eyes of the man in the picture, young, handsome, wide welcoming smile, looked like a charmer, eyes penetrating, enigmatic, as if they could bore deep into your soul if he wanted to. Allen met people like him before, not this strong, and always came away disturbed by what he saw. "I want to meet him and yet in a vague way I don't."

"I let him talk for a while," Doc said." He's got an ego that won't stop, bragged a lot about his accomplishments. He talked a lot about reforming the financial system around the world."

Doc sat still a moment as if waiting for a comment from Allen, then continued. "What are you thinking?"

"I'm not sure how a high-level world financial leader fits in with my preaching, especially one from France."

"I'll tell you one more thing about him. He's well connected, but he struck me as sly, not giving me more information than he thought I needed. I also sense a dangerous streak in him, well-hidden but there."

"Maybe that's what I saw in his eyes, Doc."

"Watch out for him, Allen. He's ambitious. I can't say for sure where he'll end up next but I'm certain he underestimated me."

"You can guess what he's up to?"

Doc smiled. "We'll see what happens. You keep working on the prophecies and giving those powerful sermons. I'll be there each time you preach a Major Sermon. Be sure to watch the news."

✝✝✝✡✝✝✝

Allen went to the office early Tuesday to work on his sermon for the coming Sunday. He kept the television in his office on all day to keep up with the news.

As he expected, nothing seemed clear. The first thing he noticed, contrary to most major military events, nobody took credit for the attack. Odd, he thought.

An hour later the reporter said officials in China and Europe speculated the United States, in coordination with NATO, may have unleashed a secret weapons system. The US denied any involvement.

Later in the morning the first word from Israel arrived. The official release said the attack surprised the sophisticated military detection systems of the IMF.

Around noon, the Prime Minister of Canada suggested a catastrophic equipment failure caused the minimal destruction reported.

By afternoon, a few reports started to come in. The American Defense Department announced it would release satellite imagery later in the day.

Strangest of all, not a word from any of the radical Islamic groups around the world. This silence astonished most of the reporters since these groups always took responsibility for any disastrous events related to Israel.

A reporter in Jakarta tried to contact one of these cells in Indonesia but couldn't locate any of the members. Where did they go? He also talked with a few Muslims on the street in that heavily Islamic country. Every one of them said they saw nothing. One who tried to go to his mosque said he found it heavily damaged and unusable.

†††✡†††

Tuesday evening at home, Allen and Joanne watched the news. At 6:15, one announcer cut into the regular news flow.

"We received the satellite photos of the Middle East and they're shocking. For the last two days we've heard no news out of the area but now the situation is clearer. Look at the area around Israel. From the Jordan River to the Euphrates we see light green, as if grass is growing in the desert. We've talked with a few agricultural experts, but nobody knows why this happened."

He stopped, grabbed at a sheet of paper an aide brought onto the news set. "Here's a bulletin. A plane flew over Mecca and Medina. This is horrible, amazing. Both Temples are rubble, you can't see the Kaaba, it's gone, destruction everywhere. A few people are out in the streets, walking as if in shock. We see bodies everywhere. This is incredible. We've tried to contact the Saudi government in Riyadh but no answer. Wait a minute, new pictures coming in. Riyadh, omigosh, ruins everywhere. The Saudi royal palace and administrative buildings are rubble, smoking from huge fires."

The program went to a commercial. "Figures," Allen said. "Gotta make money even when the world is falling apart."

The news anchor returned. "New photos coming in droves. I'll be general because I'm getting too much. Many Arab and Muslim capitals directly surrounding Israel are selectively destroyed, we can't reach governments because maybe those governments don't exist anymore. Russia is a mess, north African cities are in shambles, we heard rumors about a few eastern European countries also, reports of mass destruction from Germany." He stared into the screen. "I'm almost speechless. This is beyond anything anyone ever saw, huge swaths of utter destruction, bodies everywhere, military equipment smashed, cities in rubble, smoke, and fires everywhere but in only certain demographics. It looks primarily like radical Islamic countries and sites around the world are decimated. I can't begin to describe..."

He stared at the wall exhibiting the satellite photos.

Allen looked at Joanne. "It's happening," he said. "Prophecy 13, the Ezekiel attack, as I described per the Bible on Sunday." He felt a sudden weight lift from his shoulders.

††† ✡ †††

Allen watched another news show Wednesday about noon. Developments arrived in small batches after the overwhelming news of the day before. Overnight and early in the morning, more reconnaissance flights revealed more massive destruction.

The reporter said, "We know more about the major disaster of the last few days now. In examining the devastation, it's beginning to look like whatever or whoever did this acted with almost surgical precision. They destroyed government buildings in major Islamic capitals but neighborhoods around them remained intact. Radical Mosques suffered a major blow. Remember those armies Israel told us they believed secretly amassed and approached Israel from all sides? The ones nobody saw. It appears they did start to invade; they're all dead just outside the Israeli borders. They never entered. How was this possible? The numbers of the dead range into the millions, Israel did nothing, the invasion caught them by surprise. What a mystery! As far as we can determine, the governments of about 40 Middle Eastern, eastern European and northern African countries no longer exist. We see minor rioting in the streets, but mostly people act bewildered and wander aimlessly. One thing is clear, the destruction targeted only radical Islamic portions of these countries and their facilities. Another unusual thing, we heard nothing from extreme radical Islamists anywhere. The only people left appear to be the faithful non-radical Islamic citizens. Make no mistake, something decimated a major religion, destroyed its holy places, millions of people, mostly military, government officials, and radical Islamic groups, killed. By whom? Nobody knows. This happened within hours, and then … was over. How is this possible? This is a catastrophe of, to use a cliché, Biblical proportions."

Allen turned off the television. He'd heard enough to know what he wanted to do the next Sunday.

†††✡†††

On Thursday morning's news, Allen heard the President of the World Bank resigned in the aftermath of the devastation. The reporter continued, "The President of the United States, who usually appoints the new president, decided not to make an appointment. The devastation in Europe and the Middle East required a person from the area to take this position, he told reporters. He consulted earlier today with several European leaders and they announced the surprise appointment of a new Bank President. We're confused by the choice, a new board member from France, where he is involved in local banking in Paris, Guy Terrestre. We're looking into his background because this is such an important post in this moment of world peril. We'll pass along more information as it becomes available. Mr.

Terrestre always declines to make himself available to the press. Oh, here's a bulletin. Mr. Terrestre scheduled a major speech Friday morning about his plans for the bank."

Allen turned off the television again. He spent the rest of the afternoon preparing for the meeting of his Prophecy Group, knew the events of the day made the meeting a crucial, major turning point.

5

PROPHECY GROUP MEETING

Thursday afternoon, after contemplating the week's events, Allen decided to hold the Prophecy Group meeting at the church instead of one of the member's homes for security reasons. So much happened and the world fell into such a state of jitters that he knew his planned Sunday sermon would set off alarm bells, where he wasn't sure.

He texted everyone to arrive at different times but to be ready to go at 7 p.m. He'd bring snacks.

Allen arrived at the church early, went to his office in the building behind the sanctuary. As he walked across the silent, empty church campus, he wondered how long the church could remain here in this facility. What kind of crowd would show up next Sunday? He'd get the church staff on the problem.

What a difference four days made. Allen saw his life shifting in dramatic fashion, his passion for prophecy turned real, the return of his old friend Doc, the conviction God knew what He was doing, knew He'd placed Allen in a strategic position.

Before this moment, his group consisted of a gathering of a small number of influential people from the church, but only their passion for prophecy mattered to him at the time. Now their influence mattered. For the first time Allen realized how deep his small group's connections reached into society.

He thought about each one. Eric Newton, one of the earliest members of the group. His ready laugh always broke up serious moments in the meetings, a buddy to all the group members.

Officially, he was one of the most influential members of the group, a full bird Colonel in the Marines and a confidante to members of the Joint Chiefs of Staff in Washington. He chose to live in Illinois and work at the local Marine base to stay close to his family. How could Allen know a man with influence in the top levels of the US military? Not by chance.

The next member of the group, Todd Proctor, served as the local district Congressman, a member of the US House of Representatives and a member of the House Appropriations Committee and the Intelligence Committee.

Allen wondered at his good luck, or maybe it wasn't luck. Todd knew the Secretary General of the United Nations, based in New York City. He knew the President of the United States and a few foreign leaders, including surrogates of the French President. This week he happened to return to his district, ready to attend this most crucial of church meetings.

Then there's Sam Gold. He's the local police chief, a big position in local government but not usually a person with a national reputation. Before coming back to Illinois, Sam served in both the FBI and the CIA and retained connections in both agencies. He's closely tied into national law enforcement changes as they happen.

Then he turned to Mike Christensen, president of the local bank but deeply connected with Wall Street after years as a stock trader and investment banker. He also knew three members of the Federal Reserve Board and developed strong connections with the World Bank board. Allen wondered if he'd ever heard of Guy Terrestre.

Mike knew how to steer the group through the financial changes Allen knew were coming and keep them up to date on the new one world economic system that was about to arrive based on prophecy.

Last, Bill Wright, the local surgeon. Bill's background included graduation from one of the most prestigious medical schools and membership in several major medical boards. He gave the group medical protection since he could access certain medical procedures and medications even if the world restricted them, as Allen already knew might happen from prophecy. He was vital in protecting the church staff and members during the Virus crisis. Again, incredibly good fortune.

And, of course, John Josephs, his closest friend from his earliest days with Doc 42 years earlier; an incredible preacher in his own right. John stayed with Allen though the most difficult parts of his early ministry and stuck by him while he built his church.

With humble recognition, he wondered at the incredible group of people God put together for this important moment, the impending return of Jesus Christ to earth, with so many specific players at such a high level of connection in their respective fields. How was this possible? God is amazing.

He thought back to a verse in the Bible, which revealed in the last days they would need to be *"shrewd as serpents and innocent as doves."*[113] This verse from Matthew, he thought, must become a guiding motto for his group of experts and connectors.

God knew this all along. It wasn't mere chance.

Allen heard footsteps in the hall outside his office, opened the door. All six men plus John's wife Alice and Joanne walked in, silently, as if they all knew the burden each must now assume.

When everyone settled in, Allen said, "By the grace of God, here we are, ready to take on the most momentous challenge in the history of the world. God brought us together at this time to do His work, based on His prophecy. I'm humbly grateful for your presence tonight.

"Before we go any further, I need to make an announcement I wanted to make years ago. As of today, John Josephs will become the second Senior Pastor at this church. Last week was the first of five Major Sermons I will give over the next couple of years, this coming Sunday will be the second. John will split the Sunday preaching times with me between this coming Sunday and the final three Major Sermons. John, you've no idea how your strong friendship influenced me over the years. I welcome you as an official partner in this church."

Everyone in the room stood and applauded.

John said, "I accept your appointment with humble gratitude. We know we live in serious times, filled with

---

[113] Matthew 10:16

peril but also with the love of God for His Church and for His Chosen People, the Jews. We know the next few years will try us greatly. We also know they will bring us deep blessings and joy as we take the Prophetic Word of God to as many people as possible before His arrival."

"Thank you, John. Now down to more mundane considerations, Sam, what are your thoughts about security for us?"

Sam said, "I've long thought about this. With such a huge congregation and so many people none of us know showing up every Sunday, there's always the possibility of unpleasant incidents. I'm planning to do a full security review and will present a plan next week. More urgently, we need a traffic plan for this Sunday."

Allen said, "I'll set up a meeting for Saturday with the staff and we'll make sure the plan happens. Can you also contact your friends in the FBI and CIA to see what the buzz in those agencies is? I'm particularly interested in any possible law enforcement actions."

"Yes, I'll do that too."

"Todd, I heard the House called a special session for Monday. Can you fill us in?" Allen said.

"The United Nations is more important right now," Todd said. "I talked to my friend the Secretary General yesterday. He said they plan to call a special session for next Monday to discuss the situation. He said he's heard no reaction from almost a third of the UN member states, mostly Islamic countries. Their governments don't appear to exist anymore. I also know he wants to set up an international operation to handle the huge humanitarian crisis the events of last Sunday in the Middle East created.

They're spooked because nobody can figure out what's behind the disaster. Except us."

"Be sure to attend the special session of Congress next week and keep us posted," Allen said. "Eric, is there an update on the military situation?"

"The latest I heard all branches of our military are confused," Eric said. "We stationed troops in Iraq and Syria and a few in Bahrain, including a few of my Marine buddies. Near as we can tell they are all alive and well but surrounded by destruction. It's hard to move anywhere in those countries because the roads and railroads are heavily damaged and the ports unusable. They are sending transports to get those men out of the area."

"Mike, the markets went volatile the last few days. Any insights on what's happening?" Allen said.

"Nobody expects them to settle down anytime soon. This is a similar reaction to what occurred in the early days of the Virus but with the apparent loss of many countries, there seems to be no confidence based on recent historical events that multiple world currencies will be able to sustain any kind of vibrant world economy. The problem is severe this time. We're looking to the World Bank to stabilize European markets, but their resources are limited. They work with other agencies, particularly the International Monetary Fund and the World Trade Organization, to make things happen," Mike said.

Allen said, "I heard the World Bank installed a new president and he's giving a speech tomorrow morning. Strangely, he sent me a registered letter earlier this week saying he was interested in my sermons. His name is Guy Terrestre. Do you know anything about him?"

Mike said, "I actually met him once when I was in Europe. He's dynamic and charming, a real go-getter and comes from a well-connected family. He made it clear all financial agencies needed to work together to solve these collective world financial problems. I think he wants to reform the currency exchange system to make it work better. My friends tell me he plans to make an important announcement tomorrow, but he's kept it secret for the time being. Because of the events of the last week, the financial markets are in turmoil and many currencies simply don't exist anymore. He wants to take fast steps to solve this problem and I'm afraid he's so persuasive he'll go too far."

Allen said, "Doc's teachings tell us the nations, the church, and the world's finances will consolidate soon. I'm including those items in my sermon for Sunday. It's coming, One World Government, One World Church, Unified Currency, over the next few months. We must remember and let our church know this is not bad news. It is incredibly good news. God is at work as He has shared with us in prophecy."

John said, "We covered the world, let's get back to prophecy, our guide for the next several years. Prophecy 13[114] happened this week. Indisputable. We no longer discuss theory in this group, we talk reality, real events in the real world. We know what must happen, step by step. I don't know this for sure, but I believe Guy Terrestre will play a major role. He's too highly placed in financial circles and at the centers of power. We need to pay serious attention to him."

---

[114] Ezekiel 38-39:16, Psalm 83

"I agree, John," Allen said. "I'm going ahead with the sermon Sunday, no holding back. It's the most important sermon I've ever given."

Allen sat silent for a moment, absorbed the enormity of the discussion. He could think of no more to say. Finally, he said, "Thank you everyone for being here. I'd like to close with a prayer."

Every member of the group held hands in a circle, stood, closed their eyes. Allen said,

"God, we pray that You give us the strength to carry forward our part of Your plan for this earth, that You stand with us, guide us, protect us through the next months and years until we are all together with You in heaven. In the name of Jesus Christ, Our Savior, Amen."

Everyone squeezed the hand he or she held, let go. They departed in silence, each immersed in his or her own thoughts.

Allen and Joanne sat side by side on the couch in his office, contemplated the journey both began together this day. Finally, Allen said, "What a long day. Let's go home."

✡††††††✡

Friday morning at 10 a.m., Allen turned on the television in his home office. He and Joanne watched as the announcer said, "And now we bring you a special presentation from the new president of the World Bank, Mr. Guy Terrestre will bring us up to date on the world financial condition and on his plans for the future."

The scene shifted from the newsroom to the President's office at the World Bank headquarters. Guy Terrestre sat at his wide desk, dressed in the black suit and white shirt bankers often sported.

"He's a handsome man," Allen said to Joanne. "Strong presence." Something in the man's eyes caught his attention, he couldn't tell what, but it disturbed him.

Guy Terrestre began to speak. "Good morning," he said. "It's a pleasure to speak with you this morning as the new President of the World Bank. As you know, a major event occurred, I can't say war because nobody knows what happened. This event destroyed many minor and major currencies and disrupted the flow of financial assets around the world. The event destroyed many banking connections and other banks froze all transactions until the situation became clearer.

"Today, I'm announcing a major initiative from the World Bank, which does not at this time control international finance, to connect with the International Monetary Fund, the World Trade Organization, and individual reserves in various nations, including the Federal Reserve in Washington, to deal with this desperate situation. I wish we could snap our fingers and make it go away, but we cannot. For the good of the people of the world we must find a way to restore normal banking functions so commerce can continue smoothly in areas not affected by the devastation.

"Meanwhile, the World Bank, as its major task, will undertake aid missions in countries irreparably damaged by the events last Sunday so the survivors can reenter the world markets as soon as possible.

"These actions will need strong coordination between all international and local national agencies. I'm dedicated to help us successfully negotiate through this crisis together.

"Thank you for your attention."

Allen turned the television off, turned to Joanne. "He's one of the players, I'm not sure how or what his role is but I'm certain we will hear more from him in the future."

"Remember, he already knows who you are," Joanne said.

"The letter. Yes, I know." A sudden feeling of inadequacy hit Allen. He quickly pushed it away, said, "I need to go to the church, get to work on my sermon."

6

SERMON 2 -PROPHECIES 14-17

After Allen's Thursday night Bible study group, he overflowed with joy and excitement. The time to share his knowledge of prophecy arrived and overwhelmed him with its possible scope.

On Friday, after he listened to Guy Terrestre's speech with Joanne, Allen brushed up by reviewing his collection of books and notes on Bible prophecy from his time with Doc. He found everything familiar, all of it memorized. He knew his subject. In this changed world, was he up to this task? Did God want him to do this?

Finally, he called his management crew, confirming their scheduled coordination meeting at the church facility for Saturday morning.

††✪✪✪††

Saturday morning, Allen and John met with the church management crew. After the week's events proved Doc's teachings on the last days to be correct, Allen was inundated with calls from around the world, so many he installed a sophisticated system to take all the messages.

John said, "The people call you a new prophet."

Allen shook his head. "No! We must stop that thinking immediately! The items I shared last week weren't my own predictions, they included a thoughtful trained assessment of what God told mankind to look for in the Bible. I'm a simple pastor, not a prophet in any sense of the word. I illuminate the Word God already shared with us. God doesn't need new prophets today. John, we need to put out a press release. Please make sure it includes the fact that God completed His 'perfect' exposition of events to come in the last days in 1 Corinthians[115] and within the conclusions of the book of Revelation written by John the revelator."

"I'll be sure to do it." John said.

Allen continues, "As we discussed earlier, we're going live on television every Sunday from here out. All set up?"

"Yes. We're ready to go, plenty of extra bandwidth starting this week."

Allen turned to the facilities manager. "Are we ready for tomorrow? If you thought last week's crowd was big, wait until tomorrow morning." The facilities manager said, "We expect the 10,000-seat sanctuary to overflow. In addition, we created another 10,000 seats in the adjoining assembly rooms along with multiple major patio courtyard spaces on the church campus with sound systems and monitors. I've put on extra parking monitors to deal with nightmare traffic."

---

[115] 1 Corinthians 12:7-11, 13:9-11

Allen said, "I already decided we'll need more sanctuary space in the future. John, you said you knew someone with a much larger facility."

"I talked to him yesterday. He's a philanthropist and large donor. He offered to give us his local 40,000 seat convention hall, complete with a full built-in, state of the art television studio far better than ours. We can use it for no charge into the future if you decide you need it."

"We need it. I'll personally graciously accept and thank him for his generosity."

"One other thing," John said. "A lot of churches informed me they will take a live feed of your sermon tomorrow morning."

"One more thing," Allen said. He turned to the music director. "My message every week is so critical we need to dedicate the entire service to God's coming events. No more music or praise singing. People need weekly assurance that what they witness is truly God at work and they will be OK. So many churches, including ours, I confess, gave such weak preaching over the last 35 years that much of the church remains weak in faith. That stops today. Mainstream Christianity has already begun to push back against what I preach. They say it flies in the face of what contemporary churches blindly accepted as facts for many years. I'm okay because the Bible can speak for itself. God will offer proof as needed in the fulfillment of His prognostications I'm sharing. Ignore the criticism. Any other thoughts?"

Nobody spoke up.

"Okay, let's get to work."

††✿✿✿††

After the staff meeting Allen went home, found Joanne waiting for him. "How did your meeting go today, honey?" she asked.

Allen said. "I must admit I'm overwhelmed about where I go from here. I know Doc trained me for this moment, but last week's events catapulted me to a level I never thought possible. Am I up to the task? Did I bite off more than I can chew?"

"Allen, I understand your concern," Joanne said. "Let's pray about this together like we've always done. We're a team, we come together whenever you feel doubts. God will give us His answer."

"Wow! Honey, you are truly the angel I married 35 years ago. I love it when you whisper truth into my ear."

After dinner Saturday night, Allen went to his home office to finish a final review of his outline for the Sunday sermon. After reviewing the outline, late Saturday night, he leaned back in his comfortable chair to relax before going to bed. He felt well prepared for his second Major Sermon in the morning.

††✿✿✿††

Allen let his body relax, fell into a deep sleep. A dream vision slipped into his sleeping consciousness, real, no ordinary dream. He heard Doc's voice and saw his image above him. The words echoed.

In Doc's most serious voice, he heard these words, "Allen, God preselected you to be the man who will share prophetic truth with the world for several years in the last days. The prophecies you learned from God through me will play out and lead to a visual return of Christ in the clouds, not in secret as the church today erroneously accepts as proven truth."

Allen listened intently, frozen by sleep, wide awake to God. Doc's voice continued, "God guided you to establish an amazing church and television ministry for this purpose. God prepared your congregation's hearts for what He will share with them through you in the near yet short future. The Holy Spirt will guide you to confidence and boldness when you share His Word. Don't ever hold back. God will protect you so you can get the message out to as many people as possible right up to a few weeks before the day the Lord returns. Here's the key, watch for the arrival of the scourge. As of now, starting tomorrow you will become the Pastor of the Last Days. God will give you a sign that what I tell you now is real and true, not your imagination. Go in peace and boldly fulfill your destiny in the name of Jesus Christ."

Allen woke abruptly, felt sweat on his forehead, sat wide awake, remembered Doc's extremely encouraging, and highly inspiring words. Allen got up from bed, went to the kitchen to make a cup of coffee, went to his office to make final notes. He remembered Joanne sleeping in the bedroom, returned to his notes, engrossed in what he planned to say in the morning.

About an hour later, Joanne woke up. Allen heard her walk into the kitchen, sensed a quick thought: she's making her usual morning coffee. Was the night gone already? He saw a glimmer of brightness through his office window, the first glimmering of the new day, Sunday morning. He set his notes aside, wanted to share his amazing dream with her.

He heard her walk out of the kitchen toward the dining room. He stood, marched to his office door, met her in the dining room as she turned on the light.

Joanne looked up at him. He saw a moment of shock pass across her expression, heard her coffee mug crash to the ground. She gasped, covered her mouth with both hands as if in shock.

"Honey, what's wrong?"

She stood in silence, as if she knew he wouldn't believe what she was about to say. She dropped her hands to her side, said in a trembling voice, "You might want to look in the mirror."

"Why?"

"Trust me, go look in the mirror."

"Fine," Allen said. He walked into the bathroom off the dining room, turned on the light.

"Oh my," he whispered. In the dream Doc told him God would give him a sign to show what he heard was true, not his imagination.

Allen stared into the mirror to make sure the image he saw was truly him. He ran his hand through his hair. His jet-black hair turned white overnight.

Allen walked out of the bathroom, saw Joanne coming out of the initial shock."

"What happened, honey?" she asked. "How did your hair turn white?"

"Sit down and I'll tell you about what I thought was a dream last night. I saw Doc in the dream. He said remarkable things. He said God would give me a sign to show what he said was true." He rubbed his hand through his hair. "It looks like this is the sign."

They sat together on the living room couch and talked. Allen related the dream in detail, and she listened with a fascinated expression.

When he finished, Joanne took both his hands in hers, smiled, said, "The new hair is appealing… God did good."

††✧✧✧††

Sunday morning, people packed the entire Church facility. One week had passed since the attack, "the Sunday," as Allen began to call it.

No band and no praise team appeared on stage this morning as agreed in the staff meeting Saturday morning. In the quiet facility, the large crowd seemed confused.

Only the pastor's familiar podium stood in lonely view. Nobody else appeared on the stage.

All the television cameras focused on the stage and the single solitary podium at the center as the start of the service at 9:30 a.m. sharp approached. The large auditorium remained silent until a loud recorded statement began to play over the sophisticated state of the art sound system.

"Welcome to everyone who is present in the auditorium and on television from the Kingdom Today Center."

The television monitors around the auditorium focused on the stage and the prominent podium at the center. Doc sat in his usual front row seat as he did for all Allen's Major Sermons.

The announcement continued, "Let's give a warm Kingdom Today welcome to our senior pastor, Allen Rogers."

Applause erupted in the overflowing auditorium. Allen walked on stage out of a dark back corner. As he entered the room, a spotlight shone directly on him. The applause came to an abrupt halt, which Allen expected. He wore well-shined black dress shoes, black slacks, a classy black t-shirt, and a dark grey sport coat, which contrasted with his brilliant white hair! Allen felt the confusion in the audience. They must wonder why this strange man walked onto the stage and where their pastor Allen went. Allen walked to the podium, said, "Hello. I'm Allen Rogers, let's pray.

"Dear Lord, open our eyes today, that we may behold wonderful things out of your law. In Jesus' precious name, Amen." [116]

He said, "Before I start my formal sermon, you must wonder what happened to me. You may notice a slight change." He pointed to his head. "I'm adorned today with a new hairdo. It's a long story but I'll be brief." He hesitated a moment. He didn't want to mention Doc, who acted as God's messenger. Better to attribute the message to the true source.

"In a dream last night, an angel told me God selected me for a specific role in the last days, to share Biblical

---

[116] Psalm 119:18

prophecy with the masses, and said God would give me a sign indicating what the angel told me in the dream was true and not my imagination. Last night I went to bed with my beloved jet-black hair and this morning my new coloring arrived. I take this to be my sign. What I experienced last night was not a dream, it was a Godly visitation. Regardless, I take my new assignment for God and all of you seriously. We will use a new format for my services from here into the future on Sundays. God appointed me the Pastor of the Last Days."

He stood in silence for a moment.

††✡✡✡††

"Thank you for being here," he said. "Your presence means more to me than you can ever know. And to everyone watching via television, welcome from wherever in the world you reside. One housekeeping item: We will not take a formal offering with ushers any longer. Because time is important now, we provided kiosks in the back of the auditorium for offerings. Please give what you feel God places on your hearts, I'm going on faith here into the future.

"The Psalm/Ezekiel attack, Event 13 I discussed last week, arrived. As you see with your own eyes, news accounts confirmed that all the items related specifically to Israel I shared with you occurred this week. God performed this miracle for Israel by Himself as revealed in the book of Ezekiel.[117]

---

[117] Ezekiel 38 – 39:16

"I offer some great news this morning. My good friend, pastor John Josephs, has been elevated to co-senior pastor at Kingdom Today Center."

The congregation rose to offer a standing ovation for this great man of God.

"Every week, from here on out, between my Major Sermons, John and I will trade off on teaching. We will include current event updates in our weekly sermons.

"Today is my Major Sermon #2 in a set of five major important prophetic messages I will personally give over the next couple of years. The fifth final Major Sermon will be delivered shortly before we see the return of Christ. This timing for these Major Sermons will become clear as we move further into God's final prophecies. We will know with some precision when the Lord will return because God will guide us. I know this sounds impossible, but I'm asking for your patience and to trust me on this.

"When we advertise a future address as a Major Sermon, please pay specific attention and join us with as many family members and friends as possible to listen to what I plan to share on those special days.

"Last week's attack represents God's two-minute warning for mankind, indicating the second coming of Christ will take place after He fulfills 11 more prophetic events, all in ways far more spectacular in scope than what the church, through apathy, ever considered possible.

"This next statement will shock many of you and will fly in the face of unsubstantiated traditions the church has blindly accepted for generation. I will prove what I will share on this subject over time using only the Bible itself as my reference source. Here we go ...

"Jesus does not intend to return secretly and instantly but will visually arrive for all the world to see[118] in a spectacular set of purposeful events with great multiple meanings and significance. I will show you how and why in detail during this process. God always does things in a big way. Event 13's arrival this week proves this for those who may harbor doubts. I will save how Jesus plans to arrive for a later major message, so stay tuned. It will be fantastic, it will be … Epic. All glory be given to God.

"In today's sermon, I will share details about the next four prophetic events, prophecies 14-17. This will allow God to confirm for us visually that these things will indeed represent His plans by design. God gets all the glory because He clearly states these events in His Bible. I'm only the messenger; I am not a prophet!!! We know in advance what will come because God told us so that when we see things happen, we can believe. God will prove the reality of these coming events on His own.

"Some of the events in prophecies 14-24 might at first blush instill fear or dread, but only in those who do not know or want to accept that what happens is God's plan. This fear is not what God intends for us; it never was. He gave us these prophecies to tell us and show us things in advance with four major purposes:

"First, so we know what's coming and why in the last days during our short remaining time on Earth before the Lord returns.

"Second, so we can live in peace and joy within the new realities He told us will come without fear, but with amazement.

---

[118] Joel 2:30-31, Luke 21:25-28 emphasis on 27-28, 1 Thessalonians 4:13-18

"Third, so we can share what we see with our family and friends and especially the Jews so as events happen God gains credibility when He shows the world what we learned from His Bible is accurate. We must be bold yet humble at the same time and give God all the credit. What we see will be wonderful if we keep our minds on God's reasons for events to occur.

"Fourth, best of all, when we get close to the 24th event or prophecy, I'll show you how God made a special request of all Christians for moments before His literal visual return.[119] Yes I did say visual so bear with me. God tells us we will get a Crown[120] for knowing what to do and when to do what He asks of us on one specific day. I will show you how we'll know the day of His arrival, possibly mere hours before His return only on the actual day His arrival will occur and how this is possible; it is awesome!!![121]

"God created multiple purposes for Jesus' return for His church to occur visually. They're so incredible Cecil B. DeMille never thought up anything more spectacular. For younger people, look Cecil up. I'll show you the multiple reasons God gives us in the Bible why He will not arrive secretly but visually on a grand scale.[122] It's all in the Bible.

"I know many of you and much of the church today holds to an antiquated theory called imminence, which says the Lord can only return in secret to take this church home with him. This is how the church can justify a pre-Tribulation Rapture. The great news is that God's plans for

[119] Luke 21:27-28, lift-up your heads, this is literal with a purpose as proposed
[120] 2 Timothy 4:8, crown of righteousness, for knowing when to lift you head.
[121] 2 Peter 1:19, 'day star,' King James version, for this translation.
[122] 1 Thessalonians 5:1-11

His Son's return are incredible. When I say the event when Jesus takes us with Him to heaven will be a visual event, not secret, to many of you I may sound like a heretic. I also know a few of you might at this moment desire to stand up and leave this service thinking I may be ill informed or loony, but I humbly ask you the following two questions. Which concept of the Lord's return will give Him the most glory and majesty possible and have the most dramatic possible effect for His glory on the world: a secret quiet weak instantaneous surprise return or a grand multi-purpose visual event?[123] Jesus' visual return will be incredible to behold and can in no way be in secret as it would not be in God's character. The second question: The Bible says, "We will all be changed in a moment in the twinkling of an eye," but when are we changed?

"The answer might surprise you. This happens at the Lord's return to take believers home with Him before His 7-year period of judgments come upon the world as we all know and expect. But did you know six things will happen when we see the Lord return in the clouds first? These six things must happen before we are changed in the twinkling within possibly a few minutes, and they all have reasons to occur. The seventh event is the one that will take your breath away, literally, and figuratively!

"This set of events is so specific and so special we will be blessed to get to see them. After we witness the first six events, in the seventh event God changes us, all of us He took with Him into the sky, in a twinkling of an eye, not before. What the Bible shares about this is incredible.

---

[123] *Stunned,* 2015, Blomgren, entire Chapter 6 pages 173-218. 151 verses from 19 different books of the bible to create this well documented hypothesis.

"The Bible does not say anywhere directly that the Lord's return will be a surprise secret taking. This is pure supposition and a weak one. On the contrary, I believe I will prove God is telling us the opposite. I will share this in detail in the future in Major Sermon #5 where I will cover this one topic alone regarding the final 24th Prophecy. I'm placing the cart ahead of the horse. I hope I have intrigued you. Regardless, please do not discount this concept, have faith to think outside the box.

"Based on God's 24-event sequence, His Road Map for the last days, I believe the following four things will soon arrive. John and I will review each of these in more detail in the coming weeks as these prophecies or events 14-17 unfold. I will share them now and we will study them and watch how they play out. Here is what I believe God tells us is about to arrive based solely on Bible prophecy:

"The next prophecy is Event 14, the first phase of the conversion of Jews. God in the last days will start to bring many of them to belief in Jesus as their Messiah.

"After the attack, the world will see many Jews specifically accept Jesus as their Messiah, a small number but significant.

"This is the first of three stages of God's intended final conversion of the Jews, 'His glory,' to accepting their intended prophesied Messiah, God's Son Jesus the Christ.[124] I will share the second stage in the near future and then tell you about the third, which will happen after Jesus takes His believing family home with Him first.

---

[124] Ezekiel 39:7, *Stunned*, 2015, Blomgren, after the Israel attack many Jews will accept Christ stage 1 of 3 major conversions.

"Other things to watch for: Israel will now expand out into the surrounding land areas not destroyed in the attack last Sunday, taking the plunder from those that intended to plunder Israel in the areas where many Arabs died,[125] a land mass from the Rivers of Egypt to the Euphrates River. Israel will soon be 20 times larger in land mass than it was last Sunday. This is the land area God promised to Israel in the book of Genesis, the Abrahamic covenant.[126]

"We will learn that the Israel attack will have killed so many people the government plans to send military coroner groups to collect the bodies and body parts for disposal. Israel will tell us, as does the Bible, they estimate it will take seven months to find and mark all remains inside and around Israel to be able to complete this cleanup task.[127] This is the beginning of a set of prophetic events that will dwarf what happened as a result of the Virus. The Virus desensitized mankind to major difficult challenges in their lives. A possible positive result to the Virus, and for God's coming final prophecies.

"Something miraculous has recently happened inside Israel. Predatory birds arrived and will help naturally in this clean-up process.[128] They aren't native to this region but started to make a home in Israel beginning in the last couple of decades,[129] an unexplained phenomenon that's prophesied, we now know why.

"So much destroyed military equipment fell in Israel and surrounding regions, it created a massive cleanup

---

[125] Ezekiel 39:3-5, 11-16, *Stunned*, 2015, Blomgren, pages 127-128
[126] Genesis 15:18, *Stunned*, 2015, Blomgren, pages 83-86
[127] Ezekiel 39:12
[128] Ezekiel 39:4
[129] This is actually true today in the real world.

task. Authorities will tell us, as does the Bible, they need an estimated seven years to collect and destroy these items by burning or incineration as no place exists to dispose of so much material in any other way.[130]

"When Israel expands outward,[131] with all the adjoining oil fields and their recent finds in their current territory, Israel will quickly become the single major superpower on the planet. God provided for His people, but even today they don't understand who Christ truly is, a problem. But God the father is patient with His Glory Israel,[132] He is seriously working on them.

"In a new expanded State of Israel, the Biblical City of Babylon will now be located inside their larger state. This will now be of great significance.

"Event 15 is major rebuilding projects in Babylon. In the book of Daniel,[133] we are told about four major forms of government that will occur in the world through to the last days. The first three in history ruled out of the literal City of Babylon. We are told the final government in the last days will be located there also and this will be a sign for us to see. [134] So, the significance of Babylon being in the new larger Israel cannot be discounted or underestimated.

"Both the one-world government and church of the last days will be in the land of Shinar per the book of Zechariah.[135] The land of Shinar is literally the real Babylon, about 50 miles south of Baghdad in the land

---

[130] Ezekiel 39:9
[131] Ezekiel 39:10
[132] Isaiah 46:12, 48:11
[133] Zechariah 5:5-11, *Stunned,* 2015, Blomgren, pages 50-51
[134] Daniel 7:23-24, *Stunned,* 2015, Blomgren, pages 79-81
[135] Zechariah 5:10-11

known as the country of Iraq prior to the attack last Sunday.

"The City of Babylon will go through a major rapid rebuilding process, as this city will be pivotal for the next two prophecy events, 16 and 17. Also significant, this city will now sit inside the new large State of Israel by God's design.

"We move on to Event 16, in which a one-world government will form.[136] In the book of Daniel,[137] God tells us four successive forms of government in the world get progressively worse. Three passed and the fourth is forming today. The final form of the fourth government will take hold and we will see it end up functioning out of true City of Babylon as prophesied by God. We will see this government take hold inside Babylon soon. By the way, God says Babylon so do not think He means Rome or any other city in the world.

"Also, we are told in the book of Revelation[138] seven kingdoms will rule on the earth. Five ended prior to Christ's first visit and a sixth was in place when Jesus arrived and has existed in various forms since Christ lived until today. A derivative of this sixth form will soon consolidate into the final seventh form, a one world entity, the government of the last days, which will soon arrive. We'll see this happen. Do not worry about this if it troubles you as God told us what He is doing, and we have nothing to fear. It is all good news in God's plan.

---

[136] Daniel 2: 31-45, 2:31-43, *Stunned,* 2015, Blomgren, pages 51-52 and 79-81
[137] Daniel 7:23-24, *Stunned,* Blomgren, pages 77-81
[138] Revelation 17:9-11, *Stunned,* 2015, Blomgren, pages 72-75

"With many million dead as a result of the Prophecy 13 attack, the world will soon become overwhelmingly bewildered in severe shock. This shock would have been far worse if we have not lived through and experienced the Virus. We all learned there was life after the Virus. The same will be accepted here, on a much larger scale.

Twenty percent of the member countries of the United Nations, mostly around the Middle East, no longer exist. The world is in a state of malaise. Allow me to postulate how this may play out. We will watch world events over the next couple of months and see what transpires.

"Certain world entities controlled by backers of the World Bank feel now may be the time for all countries to come together to form a one world collective, a one world government.

"The United Nations may collectively ask each county to hold national votes to see if their populations are willing to discard their forms of government and join in one big collective. This would mean no more kings, presidents, national congresses, parliaments, or courts. The world can become one great big happy family - but people will not like it yet may accept this. Prior to the Virus the minority would reject this but not any longer.

"The World Bank will likely sweeten the pot and promise to eliminate all the national debt of any country who gives up their sovereignty and votes to join into the new world collective so they can start fresh. Not even the USA will be able to turn this offer down after the financial devastation of recent world events. The vote will be in favor of giving up the United States as we know it. A quiet revolution with no guns. We are not destroyed; we are changed and our name as a country goes away.

"A new one world money source will arrive as all money in the world will be converted into a single currency backed by the World bank. No more need for conversions of capital.

"Every person's wealth or lack of wealth in the world will be recalibrated, people can keep their houses etc., but the conversion rate to the new currency will not be equivalent in purchase power to what you saved. Those without money will get some. Sounds troubling but again remember when this occurs, we are not far from the return of Jesus, so we keep our eyes on the prize. Go along with this and do not fight it, as fighting will be a losing choice. Great events are happening, and God is in full control. This all needs to happen, and the Bible is telling us this one world government will occur.

"Remember again in Luke we are told the world will be at peace[139] until the day the Lord comes suddenly as a thief to steal away something? Is this theft the Rapture? No! It is a false peace[140] mankind will be living in when Jesus returns per 1 Thessalonians. This next statement is of the greatest importance, His return is to be a surprise only to those who do not understand God's signs, the unbelievers who do not know the Bible; but it is not intended and never was intended to be a surprise[141] to those who do know the Bible and trust God. Again, I will give you all this detail in Major Sermon #5.

---

[139] Luke 17:26-36, *Stunned*, 2015, Blomgren, pages 204-207
[140] 1 Thessalonians 5:1-11 *Stunned,* 2015, Blomgren. Pages 192-204
[141] 1 Thessalonians 5:1-11 *Stunned,* 2015, Blomgren. Pages 192-204

"One man in the world today will rise to the top of this one world government. We will soon learn who he might be. Watch with anticipation.

"This man will run the one world government at its early inception out of the City of Babylon. This will be another sign of what is happening.

"Let's move on to Event 17, when a one world church will form. For this event, I invite Senior pastor John Josephs to summarize this for us."

Allen stepped away from the podium, John stepped up.

"Good morning Kingdom Today Center, I'm John Josephs. Regarding the 17th prophetic event, we are told in the books of Zechariah and Revelation[142] that in the last days the final church, which will not be a good one in the end, will form in the plains of Shinar,[143] which is the real City of Babylon.

"The Bible also tells us in the last days two forms of churches will exist simultaneously prior to the Lord's return, the 6th and 7th forms of churches as described in the book of Revelation.[144]

"The sixth church in God's favor in Revelation is called Philadelphia.[145] Christ tells us He will take this church with Him to His Kingdom when He initially returns for us. We are part of this church.

"The seventh church not in God's favor in Revelation is called Laodicea.[146] This church will need to experience a set of 21 judgments by God in a seven-year period called

---

[142] Zechariah 5:5-11, Revelation 17:1-5, *Stunned,* 2015, Blomgren, pages 50, 52-75
[143] Zechariah 5:11
[144] Revelation 3:7-22, *Stunned,* 2015, Blomgren, page 181-184
[145] Revelation 3:7-13, *Stunned,* 2015, Blomgren, page 181
[146] Revelation 3:14-22, *Stunned,* 2015, Blomgren, page 182

known as the Tribulation explained in the book of Revelation[147] in detail. We will know this church when it forms in the land of Babylon,[148] where God says it will be located. It will not become a truly evil church until the 6th church, Philadelphia, is removed and taken to heaven by Jesus at the Rapture. We have some good indications which church will unknowingly transform and befall this fate when they form in Babylon. (Note, this is important, I will soon explain which church is in peril. If you or any family members are a part of this church today, please accept what I am about to tell you as a possible warning of what to look for. The church in existence today that fits this model will not become a problem until and unless it moves to Babylon, in the near future. This will be a significant sign to watch for. If you are a member of the church I am about to describe, and they move their headquarters to Babylon, be exceptionally careful.)

"What church might move to Babylon … soon?

"Some clues exist today.[149]

"In the Bible we know God assigned Paul as the apostle to minster to the Gentiles, specifically in Rome.[150]

"Peter was assigned to be the apostle to the Jews[151] who lived predominantly in the true real City of Babylon.

"Many today accept that Peter and Paul worked together in Rome in their ministries, because we see a sign

---

[147] *Stunned*, 2015, Blomgren, Chapter 7 pages 221-235, 7-year Tribulation, 21 judgments in total, the 7 Seals, 7 Trumpets, in the first half or 3 ½ years, 7 bowls in the second half. ½ of the world's population inside the Tribulation will die in first 3 ½ years. 7 full years of terror.

[148] Babylon is in the land of Shinar, Zechariah 5:5-11

[149] *Stunned*, 2015, Blomgren, pages 69-74, 84-86

[150] *Stunned*, 2015, Blomgren, pages 69-74, note pages 70-72, items a.- g.

[151] *Stunned*, 2015, Blomgren, pages 69-74, note page 72, items h.- k.

hanging in the Mamertine prison in Rome saying both were in a cell together, but this could not be the case. Why?

"If they worked with each other, Paul would have known Peter well. I would think he then would have mentioned him often in his New Testament writings. Paul wrote 14 of the 27 books of the New Testament. I include Hebrews for multiple reasons. In all Paul's books he only mentions Peter once briefly during a 15-day stay with him defined in the book Galatians. Nothing else in all the 14 books?

"They did not know each other well at all. Peter walked with Christ on Earth; Paul, formally Saul, did not come to know Christ until after the Lord ascended into heaven. Saul was converted to faith in Christ, by Christ in spirit on the Damascus road. Peter and Paul did not cross paths.

"Also, in the book of 1 Peter,[152] Peter says he is in Babylon with his son Mark. This was not Rome and to assume it was is disingenuous.

"Also, at about the same time, both Peter and Paul were put to death for their faith in Christ. Paul was beheaded as was the custom for Christians in the City of Rome. Peter was crucified as was the custom in the easternmost outskirts of the Roman empire … Babylon.

"Paul, upon his death, was not allowed to be buried in Rome as he was not worthy because he was Christian. The Romans buried him outside of the walls of Rome across the Tiber river where centuries later followers found his full skeletal remains in a well-marked grave. A church was built for him at his grave site outside the walls at this location.

---

[152] 1 Peter 5:12-14

The Pastor of the Last Days

"Now if the Romans put Peter put to death in Rome at about the same time, why would the Romans allow him to be buried in Rome, inside the walls, when Paul, sentenced to death for the same reason, was not? Keep this in mind as I continue, this may hold great significance.

"The Holy Roman Church built their Vatican specifically over the site where they believed the bones of Peter, who they claim to be their first pope, are located.

"Recently the Pope, the spiritual leader of the Holy Roman church, held up a small shoebox[153] he said contained the bones of Peter. A shoebox?

"Think about this, no full well-marked grave like Paul's?

"I believe this is because Peter may not be buried under the Vatican for all the reasons I shared.

"They are going to soon do major excavations in Babylon as they want to make this city grand again for the seat of the new coming one world government.

"They will discover an amazing relic, the fully accurate well-marked grave of Peter the Apostle in the City of Babylon.

"The Holy Roman church will be obligated to move their headquarters to inside the new City of Babylon where the bones of their first Pope rest.

"This new city, Babylon, will soon control world commerce.

"This new church organization will double in size because most of the remining Muslims left without a spiritual home after last week's attack are likely to join the

---

[153] This happened in the real world a few years back on November 24, 2013.

new version of this church as the ritualistic nature of the Roman Church will feel familiar to them.

"This new church may no longer contain the name Rome and will likely incorporate the name of Babylon in their new title.[154] They will quickly enroll over ½ of the world's population as members.

"They will accept everyone at first.

"They will become the one world church in the exact location where God stated in Revelation and Zechariah.[155]

"This church will rapidly start to weaken, compromising faith in Jesus alone. All other religions will be accepted with open arms but true Bible reading Christians will start to be in peril. This will happen gradually, God tells us this will happen in Deuteronomy, Galatians, and 1 Timothy.[156] Any true Christian who sees their church start to stray from full faith in Jesus alone needs to recognize what is happening and flee per 1 John and Revelation.[157]

"In conclusion, we haven't shared these issues with you to instill fear or trepidation but to inspire you, so you know what God is doing. These events are not man's work but His. We are living in the greatest moment in all of history, a time when God is talking to us vividly and openly sharing what is happening for wonderful reasons. We must give full praise to the Lord for what He is sharing with us at this moment.

John stepped away from the podium, Allen returned.

---

[154] Daniel 2:18, Revelation 17:5
[155] Zechariah 5:5-11, Revelation 17:1-5, *Stunned,* 2015, Blomgren, pages 50, 52-75
[156] Deuteronomy 18:20-22, Galatians 1:6-10, 1 Timothy 4:1,
[157] 1 John 2:18-19, Revelation 18:4-5

"Thank you, John," Allen said, "for your thoughtful exposition on the soon to arrive 17th prophecy.

"God's announcing to the world for anybody willing to pay attention that His Son is about to arrive in a spectacular way. I will share much more of God's majestic plans for His Glory Israel in the future when I share with you my three additional Major Sermons. I will announce the future dates when I will share these at the correct moments as directed by the Holy Spirit as follows.

"Major Sermon #3, prophecies 18-20.

"Major Sermon #4, prophecies 21-23.

"Major Sermon #5, prophecy 24. The grand finale ... spectacular!

"What we shared with you today will take several months to complete and place in motion. As we move forward, anticipate resistance from the coming one world church as many will not believe what we are sharing is accurate. Ignore the doubters. We also face an adversary who does not want this information known, but God wants it so we feel a strong level of protection and plan to be bold for God as modeled for us through His apostles.[158] In Matthew,[159] God also tells us to *'be shrewd as serpents and innocent as doves,'* this is wise advice for us at this time, per the book of Luke as we will come under attack.[160]

"Once God fulfills the events John and I shared today, I'll give you the next pieces of God's 24 prophetic signs in

---

[158] Boldness, Acts 9:27-28, 13:46, 14:3, 18:26, 19:8. Romans 15:15, Ephesians 6:20
[159] Matthew 10:16
[160] Luke 6:22

Major Sermon #3. It is important to me that I'm not perceived as a crazy person giving you what I think is happening out of whole cloth but provided a well-studied and fair representation of what I believe God graciously shared with us in His Bible. God is to get all the glory and if I'm wrong, I will stop but I do not believe I'm wrong. Let's see what God will do into the near future and remember, do not be afraid as our loving Father is in full control; we need to relax and go along for the ride.

"Dear Father, we trust what you are doing and that the Lord will return soon in a spectacular way by design. Offer us the proof of what I believe your word is telling us for this spectacular moment in history. Give us comfort and joy in the following months as we watch your skill in setting the table to bring your Jews to belief in Jesus your Son their Messiah. Amen"

Doc smiled 😊.

The entire congregation found themselves in awe and amazement at what they heard. Many wondered silently how the modern Christian church got so blinded and never saw God's Road Map in biblical prophecy for these last days. The truth was right before their eyes all along.

It is interesting how history seems to repeat itself. This same fate of blindness befell the religious scholars of Jesus' day, the Pharisees. They should know Jesus was the Messiah based on the fulfillment of prophecy, but pride enveloped them, and they thought more of themselves than advisable. Pride and arrogance overtook them. Is history repeating itself in these last days within the rising apostate Christian church? Highly likely.

7

PROPHECIES 14-17 UNFOLD

Monday morning, the reaction to Allen's sermon began to roll in. First, the email system collapsed under the load of tens of thousands of messages. Then the website collapsed from lack of enough bandwidth to handle the people opening the website. The phone rang incessantly.

Allen welcomed these good signs because they showed he touched a chord around the world. On arrival at the church, he called in Herman Jones, his head of technology.

"We're working hard to get everything up and running again," Herman said.

"Any idea how long?"

"It's a big job. We need to buy added bandwidth and beef up the email system. Might take until the afternoon."

"Any idea how many people saw the sermon yesterday, both live and through the website?"

"I can give you a good answer," Herman said. "We filled the sanctuary and the adjacent rooms with live attendees, around 20,000 people, about all we can handle here. The television monitoring system dropped out at about 750,000 people. Soon as we get it back up, there'll be thousands more."

After Herman left, Allen checked his favorite Christian websites, particularly the megachurches nearby. Before that attack last week, these churches saw him as a hero for the strong growth his church showed as well as his adherence to contemporary church theology.

The first blog he found was from a pastor of a large church 30 miles away. He didn't know the pastor well but met him a few times.

He read, "I've always given a lot of respect to Pastor Allen Rogers. However, this week and last week as well, he went off the rails, totally nuts. First, he went back to the old discredited prophecy themes we used to believe in, but which are no longer relevant in current church doctrine across Protestant churches. If this wasn't bad enough, he mixed up the prophetic statements with a list of prophecies I've never seen anywhere. This kind of statement confuses our parishioners, who want to hear about the loving God of the New Testament, not the frightening God of the Old Testament. I'm surprised to see Pastor Rogers fall for this nonsense.

"One especially egregious piece of nonsense is his opposition to the idea of imminence, whereas we all know Jesus will come secretly to gather his believers in the Rapture instantly, in the twinkling of an eye. The Bible states nobody can know the time and place of his coming."

Okay, about what Allen expected. Par for the megachurch movement to believe in imminence. He knew better and would continue to preach the difference. At least other Christians listened to him and yes, yesterday's sermon came as a shock to many of them, in a good way. The next few months will convince most of them as one by one Allen's illuminations of God's prophecies come true by God's hand alone, as he knew they would. Another prescient sermon or two and the Protestant community would join him.

He opened his favorite Catholic website, having no idea what to expect.

Right on the front page he saw the headline: "Protestant Pastor Teaches Dangerous Heresy."

He didn't expect much different. Everything Protestant was heresy to the Catholics.

He started reading. "Catholic doctrine is specific where prophetic events are involved. The recent sermon by Pastor Allen Rogers of the Kingdom Today Center in Illinois is clearly heretical and must be condemned in the strongest possible terms. The Holy Father long since declared the Book of Revelation to be an allegorical tale with no relevance to actual events that might occur when Christ Jesus returns to earth, as he promised 2,000 years ago. Since the Holy Father is the ultimate arbiter of doctrine, this dangerous mischaracterization of the Book of Revelation is anathema to the Holy Roman Church.

"This is a particularly ominous heresy to the Church and must be stamped out immediately wherever it appears."

Allen turned off his computer and texted Sam Gold to see him as soon as possible.

✝✝✧✧✧✝✝

When Sam arrived, Allen asked, "How soon can we move into the new building, the conference center your friend promised? We'll soon overwhelm our current facility if we continue to present the services here. The crowds keep getting larger."

"The good news is," Sam said, "the conference center is ready to move into. The facility already has a great stage, a state-of-the-art television studio and sound system, and the parking never ends. I can get a team to work today and we can start services there in about two weeks after we advertise the new location. We'll need to meet at our current facility one more time. I'll keep that service under control."

"What a relief," Allen said. "We talked about security earlier. What did you come up with? I'm especially concerned because of the larger crowds, if we check everyone into our current space, it'll be Monday before the service starts."

"I was concerned about security, but the new space includes great features I hadn't anticipated." Sam said. "We're getting a lot of pushback from your last sermon and I think you might face some danger. This will sound over the top, but we live in over the top times. Protecting you is my top priority. The whole plan will take a few weeks to get ready, but enough is available immediately in our current facility for next week."

"What's it look like for the new facility?" Allen asked.

"The Convention center already put in airport type security which every person who comes into the facility must pass through," Sam said. "We also installed 24-hour security, so nobody can get into the facility during off hours.

"Tomorrow I'll assign a team of two 24/7 bodyguards each to both you and John, along with your family members. That's how deadly serious our situation is.

"We'll get you a new podium, fully armored so if anything happens, we'll tell you through your ear-piece so you can get inside this refuge capable of withstanding high velocity rifle fire."

Allen said, "It's horrible we've come to a point in our society where threats like this happen."

"It's an age of evil apostasy. We're seeing many attacks on religious facilities today. You're sharing highly controversial material established churches, and society at large, does not take well," Sam said. "I'm also assigning two concealed armed security guards, one on each side of the stage, out of view of the parishioners, who can see the full auditorium through secret windows and act if any problems come up."

Allen said, "How soon can this be set up?"

"By next Sunday."

"What takes two weeks?"

Sam said, "I know you're not going to like this, but this part is critical. Inside our new 40,000-person center, I'm setting up a special concealed armed security force, dozens of men and women, all decorated sharpshooters fresh out of the military through consultation with Eric. We'll assign them to grids inside the convention center facility. We need to build concealment areas for them. We'll guide this top-secret force from an already existing central command facility in the convention center basement. This facility will monitor all angles of the center with infrared television cameras. The monitors can inform the entire security grid if anything happens in any sector and will inform dozens of guards who can address any problems immediately."

"This is unprecedented," Allen said. "It's a sad commentary that we need to take these steps to protect ourselves. Is there no way to get around having to make the church an armed camp?"

"I'm afraid not," Sam said. "Nobody knows what the threats are, and we can never feel safe, not from here on. You know what comes next from prophecy. We don't know how it will play out, the reason for all the security. Nobody in the church will know this force is present so it will not feel like an armed camp. Be confident security is well under control."

"Okay, Sam, go ahead and do it. I hate the idea of arming a church but you're right, we must."

Allen remembered God, in his dream, said He would protect him, so this is another added level to give him confidence to speak boldly for God in the future.

††✧✧✧††

The Thursday after the second sermon, Joanne stepped into his office. She'd helped church staff field the thousands of phone calls flooding the center switchboards.

"This is interesting," she said. "A number of Jewish members of the synagogue down the street called to say they want to learn more about Jesus. A couple said they want to accept Jesus as the Messiah based on your sermon and events since. Is this the start of Prophecy 14?"

"Welcome them," Allen said. "I expect you will see this happen all around the world, maybe even in Israel. The next prophecy to be fulfilled is Event 14, the first phase of the conversion of Jews. God in the last days will start to bring many of them to belief in Jesus as their Messiah."

"I remember your words from the sermon, 'a small number but significant' meaning enough to be noticed but not enough to wake up all the Jews yet."

††✧✧✧✧††

Allen found the news a week later more interesting. He watched it at the office with John.

The reporter said, "We've worked on this story for a week now. It appears the Israeli Army began to move a few days ago into the lands outside the borders of their country the attack didn't destroy. Millions of people used to live in these areas, but they now appear to be mostly abandoned or occupied by a small number of people. Satellite images show this new area extends from the Nile in Egypt to the Euphrates in what was formerly Iraq, Saudi Arabia, and Egypt, a huge land area. Israel will soon move into these abandoned areas and will become much larger in land mass than it was before the attack, with no resistance or shots fired.

"We already know no effective governments remain in these areas and the Israeli presence seems to be welcomed by the people who survived."

Allen said, "Rivers of Egypt to the Euphrates, the land promised to Israel in the book of Genesis, the Abrahamic Covenant as I said in Major Sermon #2."[161]

The reporter returned to the air. "We're getting confirmation of the large number of bodies found all over the Middle East, significantly most of them right outside of the current Israeli borders. Israel set up military coroner groups to collect the body parts for disposal. Israeli Intelligence sources estimate it could take up to seven months to complete the cleanup. They're reporting flocks of predatory birds in the area, attracted by the remains."

"Just as Bible prophecy told us," Allen said. "No way this is all chance."

The reporter continued. "The Israelis have other groups out cleaning up the mass of destroyed military equipment that fell in Israel and the entire neighboring Middle East region as well. Because so much destroyed equipment remains in and around Israel from the attack, the Foreign Minister stated they will need to collect and incinerate it all. They don't have enough landfills to take these items. With Israel's current smelting capability, this could take up to seven years to complete."

Someone slipped a note to the reporter.

"What's this?" He read, paused a second, read the note, stared into the camera. "Remember Allen Rogers prophecy sermon Sunday? All of this fits his predictions exactly."

---

[161] Genesis 15:18

Three weeks after the second sermon, Allen watched a bulletin announcing the appointment of Guy Terrestre as head of the International Monetary Fund and the World Trade Association. At the same time, the United Nations announced the formation of an exploratory committee to explore closer cooperation among the nations of the world to cope with the financial dislocations and political chaos.

†† ✿ ✿ ✿ ††

One month after the second Major Sermon, (the Israeli government formally occupied all the lands from the Rivers of Egypt to the Euphrates River as the Bible prophesied.[162] No resistance occurred, and this new land area became an official part of Israel. The cities of Baghdad and Babylon were now both inside the new larger State of Israel.)

In a statement, the Prime Minister said, "Since the City of Baghdad was severely damaged in the attack and is in bad shape, (Israel is exploring the construction of a new metropolitan area about 50 miles to the south in Babylon.) No other site in the Middle East presents such potential for a new major metropolitan area. Archaeologists from the Holy Roman Church asked permission to conduct an exploratory dig in Babylon, which Israel approved. Digging will begin in a week or two."

After listening to the announcement, Allen smiled at Joanne, made a checkoff motion with his right hand. "Event 15, under way."

---

[162] Genesis 15:18

†††✧✧✧†††

The promised United Nations meeting finally got under way six weeks after the second Major Sermon. All members of the Thursday prophecy group watched the televised proceedings together.

Before he turned on the television, Allen asked Todd, "Did you hear any inside information from the Secretary General of the United Nations? I heard about a ton of negotiations going on."

Todd said, "This is a tricky moment. You've got a lot of scared egos in the room. Remember, forty or more middle eastern and European governments don't exist anymore. Virtually nobody out there thinks they could cope with any kind or second attack by anybody and there's a lot of talk of general frustration, especially since Israel occupied a huge swath of the Middle East. It's not sitting well, but it's done."

The announcer introduced the meeting. "In a few moments, the United Nations General Assembly will share a proposal for creating a path to tamp down the tensions building around the world. The threats and counter threats scared everybody and are not productive. Now let's listen to the Secretary General."

The Secretary General stepped to the podium, scanned an audience far smaller than he was used to addressing.

"Good afternoon," he said, "Members of good standing in the United Nations, we face perilous times. A huge mysterious military operation nobody anticipated destroyed a large portion of the Middle East, northeastern Africa, and parts of eastern Europe, and a great deal of

140

Russia. Israel occupied portions of land adjoining their old borders, which raised questions about their ambitions in the area and brought out a group of politicians who want to form a coalition to stop further expansion.

"It is our duty to work together to stop further chaos, keep what peace remains, and bring whoever caused the chaos to justice. Sadly, I have no idea who or what the entity was.

"I've contacted members and leaders of many international financial and political organizations. All of them are scared. Nobody knows where the destroyed weaponry we see scattered for hundreds of miles originated. They are also resolute. They say to a man or woman, 'We must restore political calm to the world, we must reduce tensions across borders and bring people together.' It could take the form of a new single collective, international in nature."

A wave of muttering arose from the audience. Countries remained jealous of their sovereignty.

The Secretary General held up his hands to quiet the audience. "These times demand a collective decision. No one country can survive in a world as divided and crushed as ours. The age of going it alone is over. The World Bank tells me many nations are on the verge of bankruptcy. We are going to hold a vote today on what to do next."

The voices in the hall grew louder, more pointed, members started to shout at each other.

"Quiet!!" The Secretary General roared into the microphone. "Do you see what's happening? We're fighting each other in this hall dedicated to peace. We cannot get along!"

The delegates quieted.

"Do you see what independent governments have brought to the world? Conflict, disagreement, WAR! We are done with war. It is our duty today to find a way back to peace, back to prosperity, to a world we can again be proud of. Too many monarchs, presidents, and courts compete for advantage, afraid of each other to the point of willingness to kill their opponents. I and my backers propose to stop this recklessness, discard our independent forms of government, and come together, become a single family of mankind, to bring world peace. I propose we take a vote on the following resolution: (That the United Nations request every nation in the world to hold a national vote to surrender their current forms of government and join into a new one world collective.")

Stunned silence filled the assembly hall. Delegates shuffled paper, others stretched, then sat down.

The Secretary General said, "Secretary, call the roll of nations."

At the finish about two-thirds of the countries voted for the resolution.

"This is not good enough," the Secretary General said. "I'd like to introduce a representative of the World Bank, sent here by the bank's new president, Mr. Guy Terrestre."

A man stepped to the podium. "Thank you, Mr. Secretary General. In consultation with the president of (the World Bank, I'm prepared to offer the following. The bank decided, along with the International Monetary Fund, to promise to eliminate the national debt of any country which votes to give up their sovereignty and join the new one world collective so they can start fresh.)

"In addition, (the bank will convert all national currencies to a new worldwide currency backed by the World Bank. All money will be worth the same everywhere in the world.)

"Finally, (the bank will make sure every individual's wealth is recalibrated fairly, so everyone can compete in the new one world economy.")

The man left the stage.

The Secretary General took the podium. "This means the United Nations will go out of business, replaced by one organization to coordinate all governmental activities and financial activities in the world. Let's vote again."

The second vote went quickly and was unanimous. The Secretary General said, "Thank you. Now go home and hold your elections as soon as possible."

Allen turned off the television. Event 16, under way, exactly as he called it.

††✧✧✧††

Four weeks later, three months after the second Major Sermon, all the countries in the world reported the results of their votes to the United Nations. The UN knew this was a controversial vote and many countries would not go out without a fight.

Allen, John, and Eric watched the tally of the votes together.

("I knew a few countries, including ours, might face a problem with voters actually agreeing to give up sovereignty. However, the Virus softened the population's thinking to the idea of getting rid of all debt. The recent

143

movement in the United States towards acceptance of a socialist form of government, was a factor) Also, with the Virus, collectively doubling the national debt of the United States to a point where it could never be paid off, a fresh start sounded like a winning idea."

Eric said, "I talked with my friend in the United States Military Command yesterday. He told me the president of the World bank stepped in, informed all the militaries around the world of major repercussions if their leaders went against the wishes of the United Nations and the vote of the people."

"That's Terrestre. I'm starting to wonder about him. He's getting too much hidden power."

"He privately told all of the wavering countries he holds both the finances, resources and manpower to prevent any nation, including the United States, from overturning the people's vote to give up sovereignty."

Allen said, "What did our Central Command do?"

"My friends there tell me they did a private investigation and confirmed Terrestre holds the power to do what he says. It's astonishing anything like this was possible. How did this man amass so much power so quickly, he could overpower the United States?"

Allen, John, and Eric continued to watch the final votes officially come in. The reporter said, "I'm amazed. The votes are in and every country in the world agreed to give up their sovereignty. Remember a few days ago we reported a lot of countries didn't want to go this route. We don't know what happened since then."

John said, "Doesn't take much to figure it out. Terrestre acted like a mob boss, gave everyone an offer they couldn't refuse. The man is slick."

The reporter continued. "The closest vote came in the United States, 51% to 49% in favor of joining the collective. No real surprise since this country is often closely divided."

Eric said, "Here's one thing nobody outside knows yet. My friends in Central Command said the United States President called out the military to stop the vote. An eerie thing happened. The armored vehicles all ran out of gas at the same time. An epidemic of colds, almost like a new Virus, hit every unit called up. Nobody could function. It was like a power greater than anything they ever saw intervened to stop the most powerful military in the world from acting."

Allen said, "What a story, verifies the existence of this overpowering evil force. All Biblical."

††✧✧✧††

The next news bulletin arrived after the United Nations collected the votes. Allen, John, and Eric listened. "The Secretary General of the United Nations issued a new directive to all world leaders. Effective one week from today, (all national and local leaders, assemblies, courts in all individual states are required to resign. Anyone not obeying this order will be arrested and imprisoned."

"You don't know the half of it," Eric said. "Todd Proctor told me the Secretary General clued him in that the new world security force is run by the World Bank under guess who. Nobody knows who organized this force except us. Before this order went out, the Bank, let's say it among ourselves, under Guy Terrestre, put together a massive force in a short time. He dispatched these forces to all seats of government to ensure a peaceful transition and resignation of all leaders." No bullets, a strong armed successful worldwide coup.

After the final vote was completed and the resignation of all exiting world leaders was completed a week later, the World Bank sent out a memo to all closing worldwide government entities.

It said, ("A new system will be put in place, one more financial change. Due to the recent deadly Virus and the potential to spread germs in any future crisis to the world population, (when the coming conversion to a single currency takes place, paper money will no longer exist or be allowed and the world will go cashless. The World Government will provide everyone with Commerce Purchase Cards (CPC's) for use in their daily lives using their bank credits. Additionally, all gold, silver, and diamonds including existing cash must be turned in and exchanged within 90 days, converted, and recalibrated into new worldwide electronic credits at a rate to be established by the World Bank. After 90 days it will be illegal to maintain or hold any of these outdated monetary instruments.")

Allen said, "That completes Event 16. They've established the one world government. Nobody else knows where we go from here, but we do. For Christians this is incredible news. God already told us in advance this event would happen. Time to go along for the ride and let God guide us into our new exciting future world."

††✿✿✿††

Two weeks later, 14 weeks after the major second sermon, the final announcement Allen needed to hear arrived on another news bulletin, a simple one. The announcer said, "Archaeologists with the Holy Roman Church announced an astonishing discovery today in Babylon. For many years, the Church believed the Apostle Peter founded the Church in Rome two thousand years ago, died there and was buried there.

("Today archaeologists announced they found a fully marked tomb of the Apostle Peter in an unexcavated area inside Babylon. It's now clear Peter never taught in Rome and never lived there.

"Church authorities said little for the moment. One prominent Roman theologian told us this morning the discovery creates a foundational problem for the Holy Roman Church, which was originally based in Rome because they believed their founder, their first Pope, Peter, lived and died there. The theologian said this may require the church to relocate to Babylon, where the bones of their founder lie.")

Allen said to Joann, "This is exactly where the bad church of the last days, the Laodicean church is prophesied to be located."

The Reporter continued, "In other church news, the (Pope announced he's launched a major missionary effort in the Middle East region to preach to the millions of

Islamic people whose religion the attack decimated. Many faithful Islamic people are scared and feel alone after the attack on Israel. The Roman Church is seizing on this monumental opportunity to fill the void. The 17th prophecy is under way.")

††✧✧✧††

Three and one-half months after the second sermon, Allen and John met in Allen's office in the newly fortified Kingdom Today Church.

Allen said, "It looks like all seventeen prophecies are completed or ongoing. We have a worldwide government; we have a worldwide church forming. Time to put out the news I'm giving the third Major Sermon at the end of this month, in two weeks. That'll raise eyebrows."

John said, "Maybe more than a few."

8

SERMON 3, PROPHECIES 18-20

On Sunday Allen gave his third Major Sermon. At 9:30 sharp he stood at his podium, looked out at the massive crowd in the 40,000-seat facility, packed, standing room only. He began with his signature opening prayer.

"Dear Lord, open our eyes today, that we may behold wonderful things out of your law. In Jesus' precious name, Amen[163]

"Good morning, I'm Allen Rogers. Welcome to Kingdom Today Center."

The audience burst into a round of applause.

The applause died down. Allen said, "I'm gratified a huge number of people came to hear my third Major Sermon today. Four months ago, in Major Sermon #2, I shared details about Prophecies 14 to 17. These critical prophecies included the first stage of conversion of the Jews to Christ, the rebuilding of Babylon, Israel expanding out to control a much larger land area, the formation of the

---

[163] Psalm 119:18

one world government, and the beginnings of the one world church. All have come to pass.)

"Fortunately, with our new one-world government in place they have not yet decided to close churches. With no new world leaders in place this new government has a lot of chaos which will soon need to be brought under control. I am not sure why churches are still allowed but I think God is protecting us for as long as possible, so we continue.

"Today I address the next three prophecies. Events 18-20, of God's 24 prophecies He tells us to look for. These next prophecies will take time to complete, possibly about a year. They have major significance. Watch carefully as these events come into play.

"Remember back four months, in the Israel attack we saw the destruction of the Dome of the Rock. The Dome sat on top of the land where the Jewish Temple in Jerusalem used to be located, and where it needs to be built again per prophecy. In the attack, God purposefully cleared the land, made it ready for new construction. Please note the Temple to be rebuilt is not a good thing in God's eyes as the sacrificial system is not needed any longer. Jesus, the Messiah, was the final sacrifice, but the Jews haven't figured this out yet. They will soon.

"One of my friends in our church, Rick, is an architect. He told me it's possible the Israelis years ago created a prefabricated version of the new Jewish Temple. A few things needed to occur for this new facility to be erected, a process under way for many months since the attack.

"I'm now going to speak about Event 18, the rebuilding of the third Jewish Temple in Jerusalem.

"The construction of the new third Temple in Jerusalem needs to happen soon because of its great significance in relation to the end times. The new third Jewish Temple needs to exist before the Time of Jacob's Distress starts. My architect friend Rick also told me builders can construct a prefabricated version of the Temple quickly, possibly within six to nine months with motivation, unlimited funds and reduced red tape. Israel is motivated and will make this happen. Everything is ready to go. Miraculously, the recent Israel attack resolved the building site issue.

"When a future leader about to arrive on the scene signs a special seven-year covenant with the Jews, this will officially start the seven-year Time of Jacob's Distress period, also known as the 70th week of Daniel, which I will address shortly.[164] The Temple will be rebuilt and in place and the Jews will start to do sacrifices in the Temple again. This will be allowed into the Tribulation but will only last for a set period. Sacrifices need to happen inside the Temple, further verification the building needs to exist prior to the start of the Time of Jacob's Distress.

"This third Temple building must be given an initial blessing before it can open, achieved only through the sacrifice of a red heifer, a detailed required process described in the entire 19th chapter in the book of Numbers.[165]

"Soon after the destruction of the second Temple in 70 AD, this interesting animal, the red heifer, went dormant, not extinct, no longer needed because the sacrificial system

---

[164] Daniels 9:27
[165] Numbers Chapter 19, specifically 19:2

ended with the destruction of the second Temple. Then in 1994 a miraculous event occurred. We witnessed the birth of a red heifer—the first sighted in 1,900 years.[166] After many years now since 1994, they've grown in numbers with a small number raised kosher—close to acceptable for the sacrifice to purify and cleanse the new coming third Temple. An appropriate red heifer must be fully unblemished for this sacrifice. Does an unblemished heifer exist today? Maybe not yet. But with hundreds of thousands of them in existence at this time, it won't be long until the correct specimen arrives.

"Finally, according to the book of Daniel,[167] the Abomination of Desolation will occur inside the Temple at the midpoint of the Time of Jacob's Distress, 42 months, 1,260 days, or 3½ years in. Then a certain leader ends the One World Religion and takes claim as the only god. The new Temple sacrificial system will abruptly end 3½ years into the Time of Jacob's Distress at the Abomination of Desolation per the book of Daniel.

"We also learned all the tools required for the correct worship procedures inside the Temple are prepared and ready for use now, waiting for the correct opportunity.

"Additionally, the Ark of the Covenant will need to be here for the start of Temple worship. By faith, I believe God Himself fully protected this Ark and it will arrive on the scene soon at the right moment. There is strong evidence it may already be inside Israel in a secure location.

---

[166] This Red Heifer issue is actually true in the real world today.
[167] Daniel 11:31, 12:11, Matthew 24:15, Mark 13:14

"Everything for the new third Temple as prophesied to occur in the last days is ready to go and we will see it soon.

("Event 19 is when the One World Government breaks into 10-kingdoms.)

"After the Israel attack, we know the entire world faced brief bewilderment and disarray. We already experienced the formation of the One World Government, which happened quickly, and is our new reality. We see signs this organizational configuration doesn't work well. We need to fix this situation. We also set up the new one world currency and things aren't as bad as we originally thought, but we also know God is at work here. Remember in Luke,[168] we are told the world will live in peace until the Lord returns so this situation regarding operational control of the one world government will soon be corrected, but how?

"Prophecies or events 13-18 will have arrived or be under way, so the logical next step to fix this large one world issue will be (to break the One World Government into smaller manageable areas, controlled by appointed kings, making local control easier.)The new ruling world authorities will soon decide what to do and will tell us the number of kings and kingdoms will happen to be 10.) In Daniel,[169] we are told 'ten kings will arise;' then another will arise after them, an eleventh leader. This is a man we all need to watch for and get to know. I will address this interesting person in Event #20 later this morning. He will

---

[168] Luke 17:26-36, peace in time of Noah and Lot up to "the day" destruction came like upon them almost like a thief a thief. We are told, so will it be in the days of the son of man, the Tribulation. See 1 Thessalonians 5:1-11, with emphasis on verse 2-3.
[169] Daniel 7:24

be different from the coming initial ten kings. This 11th leader, after the initial 10 kings arrive, will be an individual prophesied in Revelation.[170] He will rule into the Time of Jacob's Distress. This man needs to be present to sign the covenant with Israel starting the Time of Jacob's Distress. All the One World Government and 10 king issues must reach full formation before the Time of Jacob's Distress can begin. We will see these 10 kingdoms form soon.

"Finally, we come to Event 20, the prophesied rise of an 11th leader, a man we need to watch carefully.

"In the book of Daniel,[171] (we are told to look for a man, an eleventh ruler who will come on the scene as prophesied after the 10 kingdoms are in place.) This indicates a time when we are close to seeing the arrival of Jesus' Catching Up event the same day as the arrival of Daniel's 70th week. This man will usher in the official final 'fourth kingdom.'[172] It's important to understand who this prophesied individual is. When I get to my last 5th Major Sermon, I will reveal the eleventh leader's ultimate identity.

"The Book of Daniel tells us the 'seventieth week of Daniel' refers to the seven-year time of Jacob's distress ruled by the coming eleventh leader. Notice how God defines in Daniel for us His word 'week' to mean seven-year periods of time. God prescribed 70 weeks (70 × 7 = 490 years) to complete His work to end all prophecy and

---

[170] Daniel 7:23-27

[171] Daniel 9:24-27, with emphasis on Verse 27. Also, note the word "flood" in verse 26 is not literal, it implies a war with a large army of many soldiers, almost overpowering.

[172] Daniel 2:40-43

sin. This period is designated for the Jews. He tells us the official start of this '70th week' happens when the eleventh ruler signs a seven-year safety covenant with Israel. There is a reason for this covenant which I'll address in Major Sermon #4. In the middle of this 70th week sacrifices stop, and the abomination of desolation arrives. This seventieth week is clearly the Time of Jacob's Distress. God does not leave us confused; no guesswork needed.

"Sixty-nine weeks (483 years) per the book of Daniel[173] in God's process were completed from the time of Cyrus' decree as addressed in Isaiah and Ezra[174] to Christ's crucifixion. Then the world experienced the Christian Age (approximately 2,000 years) for a long time out. During the time of Jacob's distress, at the start of the 70th week, I believe no living Christians will enter it by specific design; God takes believers out of the way the day it arrives. Why? Using simple logic, no Christian churches existed during the first 69 weeks. Not one true Christian church will be around for the start of the final 70th week either. This 70th week is all about the Jews.

"The book of Daniel[175] talks about a 'fourth final kingdom' that 'will devour the whole earth,' in the last days. We are told the first king of Babylon, Nebuchadnezzar, had a troubling dream — one he could not understand. He searched for a wise man to help him with an interpretation. Then God gave Daniel direction to provide the interpretation. This prophetic dream relates to the governments of the world arising between the time of

---

[173] Daniel 9:24-27
[174] Isaiah 44:28, Ezra give the timeline of the rebuilding of Jerusalem and the Temple.
[175] Daniel 7:23-24, *Stunned*, 2015, Blomgren, pages 79-81

Nebuchadnezzar, the first government, through to the second coming of Jesus to the earth when the final government will exist.

"In the book of Daniel,[176] we see the dream indicates four different forms of government are explained using the visual of a great statue of a man of "extraordinary splendor," starting at his head and moving down to his feet. The quality of these governments deteriorates based on the symbolic use of different quality metals in this dream's explanation:

"Head of gold

"Breast and arms of silver

"Belly and thighs of bronze

"4a. Legs of iron

"4b. Feet of iron and clay

"Daniel[177] lists the four groups of people who will control these types of governments. They sound like geographic locations, but no, they represent four types of governments. Historically the types of governments they represent:

"Gold, Nebuchadnezzar (Absolute Monarchy)

"Silver, Medo-Persia (Limited Monarchy)

"Bronze, Greece (Democracy)

"4a. Legs of iron, Rome (Imperialism, political Rome, in existence today; ongoing) (Western and Eastern powers—two legs)

"4b. Feet of iron and clay, is the final form of political Rome—the One World Government (Evil, final political Rome—dictatorship of the eleventh leader soon to come).

---

[176] Daniel entire Chapter 2
[177] Daniel, entire Chapter 2

"Note: The Gold, Silver, and Bronze governments ruled out of the literal City of Babylon. The next one, the final world government, Legs of Iron with Feet and Toes of Iron and clay is the final coming one world government to also be ruled out of … Babylon.

"A controversy occurs when we try to place geography into this equation. Geography will not affect the new coming final fourth Roman type of government becoming the final version of Political Rome. The legs of iron represent a political Roman form of government that started prior to the days of Jesus and continued in various configurations to our day.

"We will soon see the conclusion of this government with the 10 toes representing the 10 kingdoms of the coming final configuration of the One World Government. The eleventh ruler will reign over this final form of government out of Babylon, in the plains of Shinar.[178] As earlier explained, the eleventh ruler comes on the scene prior to the visual Catching Up and will soon arrive to claim this eleventh position. We need to watch for him since he will be a key player in the last days.

"Paul tells us, in 2 Thessalonians,[179] not to be shaken or disturbed to hear that the day of the Lord has come. The day of the Lord is yet another name for the Time of Jacob's Distress. This time cannot come until first, the 'apostasy comes,' as discussed earlier and secondly, 'the man of lawlessness,' the eleventh ruler 'is revealed.'

"The One World Government arrived, and the 10 world kingdoms will soon be in place. After we see the 10

---

[178] Zechariah 5:5-11, specifically verse 11. *Stunned,* 2015, Blomgren, pages 77-78
[179] 2 Thessalonians 2:1-3

kingdoms in place the eleventh ruler will be revealed and come on the scene.

"I believe the visual Catching Up happens on the day the Time of Jacob's Distress starts and will offer proof in a future Major Sermon. This means Christians will get to see and know who this eleventh ruler is for a short time before the visual Catching Up occurs.

"Most people in the world today won't know this dynamic eleventh leader's identity, but, as Christians, we should know. Again, I will reveal his identity, in Major Sermon #5. Others will discover his identity at the midpoint of the time of Jacob's distress. Notice, I said the eleventh ruler comes on the scene after the 10 divisions form.[180] This clearly means the entire infrastructure for this new supreme ruler must be physically in place before the Time of Jacob's Distress can start. The world cannot be in travail or in any wars, peace needs to exist for this man to be able to do his initial work. This peace is again defined for us in the book of Luke.[181]

"Remember, the events reviewed today, 18-20, will take time to fall in place. My estimate is about a year. Between today and Major Sermon #4, John and I will give weekly sermons and updates sharing how these prophecies are playing out. As events 18-20 solidify, I will announce when I will share my next Major Sermon. In this future sermon I will address events 21-23. We will be close to the final event 24 which will shake mankind to its core. This amazing event holds multiple major blessings for believers. It will also start the Jews on a final successful

---

[180] Daniel 7:24
[181] Luke 17:26-36, *Stunned,* 2015, Blomgren, pages 204-209

seven-year path to accepting Jesus at their Messiah. The Jews will tell us we're nuts, this will never happen, but I can tell you with confidence this is going to happen because God ordained it. Remember, I'm only the messenger.

"Now God please continue to bless us and keep us in your protections and give us the assurances that we are witnessing amazing things that You have shared with us in advance so that when they happen, we can believe.[182] *Give us joy and peace in the understanding of Your plans as we prepare for Jesus' return. Be with us this week Lord and guide us in these last days for Your glory alone, we pray this in the precious name of Jesus our Lord, amen."*

The entire congregation again rose to their feet and gave Allen a spectacular ovation. Allen listened; aware he was right on everything so far. He knew by the guidance of the Holy Spirit the warnings he gave them today prepared them for the next events. For all Christians, he thought as he listed to the applause, being able to know in advance what God is doing and why is the second greatest blessing God has given to mankind. All are highly loved!

Doc smiled 😊.

Guy Terrestre did not.

---

[182] John 14:29, Mark 13:23

9

PROPHECIES 18-20, UNFOLD

With the formation of the One World Government under the public auspices of the United Nations, it became clear the organization could not remain in New York City, which would create an impression the old United States, though no longer in existence, still controlled the organization.

Todd Proctor, the former US Congressman in the prophecy group, met with Allen at the church a month after the third Major Sermon to discuss the new One World Government.

Todd said, "I talked with the Secretary General earlier today. He said the only neutral and viable financial place left in the world for the government to set up its offices is within the only independent state left in the world today, Israel. He talked a lot about how the new metropolis at Babylon, already under major construction by the Israelis and the Holy Roman Church, could be a great place for the seat of government to land. It's in the eastern portion of the new larger State of Israel, the new world superpower and is central to the old European, African and Asian nations also."

Allen said, "That makes sense for Israel too. I understand they're making noise about rebuilding the Temple in Jerusalem. It's not noise, they now have permitted construction plans, as I mentioned in the last Major Sermon. I'm not surprised it's happening fast."

"The Secretary General said the United Nations as it used to exist will be terminated. Once the world's nations gave up sovereignty, all the delegates went home because they no longer represented anybody. The Secretary said he kept close contact with Guy Terrestre at the financial institutions. He knows any position he holds depends on Terrestre although Terrestre right now shows no interest in a public leadership position."

"What are they going to do?"

"I think the world government is turning out to be a bigger challenge than anyone realized. Thank heavens they put security forces in place. Integrating the economies and different social programs together amounts to a massive task. We possess the technology but so many of the local systems don't talk to each other. Tax systems no longer work and need replacement. Luckily, the World Bank finances much of this work."

Allen said, "I hear the Israelis want the Church and the World Government to take over construction in Babylon as soon as possible. I'm trying to figure out who is in charge and how they're paying for it."

✡✡✝✝✝✡✡

A week later, Israel's prime minister announced the beginning of construction of the new Temple.

"With great pleasure I announce (the groundbreaking for the new Third Temple in Jerusalem,) to be built on the original Temple Mount. We've cleared away all the rubble from the old buildings. We already started the foundations for the building, based on Biblical specifications. We will use prefabricated materials for the main building so we can build quickly.

"We'll give this project unlimited funds since it's the culmination of almost 2000 years of Jewish history in exile. We've returned home to our Promised Land, all of it, from the Nile to the Euphrates, as promised by God to Abraham.

"We expect to complete the building in about six to nine months. We will allow nothing to stand in the way of this effort."

✡✡††✡✡

Four months later, construction was well under way on (the new World Government headquarters in the new world Metropolis of Babylon, next to the new Holy Babylonian Church Cathedral) currently being built on the newly discovered site of Saint Peter's grave.

The United Nations no longer existed. It's staff, dedicated to servicing individual nations, left with little to do, was laid off. The Secretary General resigned; a new governing board took over for a short time until the organization disbanded.

Allen and John watched these developments with interest but not surprise. By now Allen knew the next prophecies would happen in a short time. Nothing surprised him any longer.

Strangely, the new One World Government seemed to operate with little staff leadership or a consolidated military force. Most of the arms held by the old nations remained in place under the watchful eyes of a new World Security Force, whose origins and leadership remained hidden.

People across the world went about their daily lives. Airlines continued to operate; private businesses proceeded without major regulation from nonexistent governments.

(Only one organization remained, the World Bank, supposedly under the direction of the One World Government.)

Mike Christensen, the prophecy group's banking contact, and Allen sat down for lunch one day.

"What a chaotic mess," Allen said. "Who's in charge, Mike?"

"I used to have a good channel into high level financial leadership groups in our early prophecy group days. Most of those organizations don't exist anymore. This new secretive government is trying to hold the world together. It happened too fast, about the only part that worked was the new world currency.) It combined a lot of the old governmental departments into new agencies but none of them work well. They're trying to get a legislative body put together."

"Who's they?" Allen said.

"Strange to say, I think most of the leadership is coming out of the World Bank. He who controls the money controls the world. But administratively it's a disaster. The good news is nobody is fighting anybody. It appears we finally brought perceived peace to the world."

A week later the answer surfaced. In an announcement, the One World Government, the OWG, naming no spokesperson, said effective immediately, the government was creating ten administrative kingdoms around the world. The OWG will appoint a king for each of these areas who will take full authority over their territory. These leaders will not be elected, they will be appointed, and they will hold their position for as long as they live. In other words, they will be kings in their domains. This will correct operational control issues, allow former governmental institutions to reform, and serve their publics better.

["Relations with these kings will be handled from the One World Government headquarters in Babylon. Peace finally arrived for the entire world. We can rejoice and celebrate our newfound peace and prosperity."

Allen and John watched this change with interest. "Event 19, as expected. I think we both know what's coming next," John said.

Allen said, "This One World Government turned out to be a great mystery. It's hard to figure out who's running it from where. These ten kingdoms make up the final configuration but where's the 11th leader?"

"I heard the ten kings formed a governing council and will choose one of their number as a rotating leader."

"No, they can't. The eleventh leader must be from outside the group of ten rulers, otherwise he's one of the ten. I think his identity will be hidden for a while but if we look carefully, we can see hints of his identity."

John said, "I keep going back to what Mike said a while back. The World Financial Organization seems to be the underlying power in the government. And who is the leader of the World Financial Organization? He doesn't say much but you see him at parties and on about every board in the world today. He's well connected and at this moment the most influential man in the world."

Allen said, "Guy Terrestre."

"I believe he's going to be the 11th leader, the man we need to watch carefully, our opponent as we go through the final four events in God's prophetic Road Map."

✿✿✝✝✝✿✿

At 17 months after the day of the attack, Guy Terrestre made an announcement to the world. The new 10 world kings appointed him the leader of their newly formed entity, The Council of the 10. Guy Terrestre officially became the eleventh ruler.

"The 20th prophecy is completed," Allen said. "I'm confident I know who he is but it's not yet time to share this information literally.

"Let's schedule Major Sermon #4. It's time."

10

SERMON 4, PROPHECIES 21-23

Since 'the Sunday' of the initial attack everything Allen taught about prophecy and the final end-time events happened. Three more prophecies needed to reach fulfillment before the day of the Lord's return. Major Sermon #4 began when Allen stepped to the podium. He offered a warm welcome and his now signature opening prayer.

"Dear Lord, open our eyes today, that we may behold wonderful things out of your law. In Jesus' precious name, Amen[183]

"Today I share Major Sermon #4 of 5. I'll explain three more end-time prophecies, events 21-23 out of 24. I estimate these will require between 18 to 24 months to develop before I share with you my final Major Sermon #5. The future fifth sermon will be out of this world!!! We'll witness amazing changes in the world during events 21-

---

[183] Psalm 119:18

23. I want you to understand what will happen and what the ramifications will be.

"Let's start with Event 21, the Time of False Peace and Safety.

"In 1 Thessalonians,[184] God tells Christians important words about a false peace to encompass the entire earth. As you can all see today, it appears we are in an odd form of world peace now that appears to be growing. To the secular world this peace appears to be a wonderful period, but future events will prove it to be a cruel deception.

"God told believers not to be surprised about what's happening in the world in the last days because He's telling us what's going to happen. We know. He also tells us the thief in the night is not the Lord taking Christians home in a secret Catching Up event. The thief in the night is entirely different. The church grossly glossed over the specific proof of this in 1 Thessalonians[185] in error, which is why they erroneously believed the Catching Up event will come in secret. (The thief issue is God ultimately stealing away this new false peace in the world the day the Lord returns.)This is of high importance; Christians are to be *in the light*[186] and must know this fact.

"For those who do not believe in Jesus, entirely different events will happen.[187] Those who accept the coming One World Government and Religion as a good thing will feel as if they finally came into a time of worldwide peace and safety. The dawning of the age of Aquarius. They won't see what's really taking place.

---

[184] 1 Thessalonians 5:1-11

[185] 1 Thessalonians 5:2

[186] 1 Thessalonians 5:4-5

[187] 1 Thessalonians 5:3

Everything is smoke and mirrors as Jesus prepares to return. The enlightened world will think of Christians as insane for not recognizing the good that appears to happen. (What appears as peace will prove, on one coming day, to be the opposite.) The secular world will literally be caught by surprise.[188] Christians will find comfort in the clear knowledge God gives them. We'll see and know what He's doing through prophecy and can be confident He will soon return.

"Now it's time to talk about Event 22, the return of Elijah.

"Before Jesus came to earth the first time, God sent a prophet like Elijah, John the Baptist, into the world to announce Jesus' arrival. He did this to give many people an advance notice, so they'd know Jesus was on the way. The announcement also provided a way to prepare people for who Jesus was, the Messiah, and His importance to mankind.

"Elijah in the Old Testament is considered the prophet of prophets, a devoted man of God who did everything asked of him with bold courage. He loved God more than life itself and remains a great example for us today. Elisha (*with an "s"*), Elijah's assistant (*with a "j"*), ultimately inherited his ministry. Elijah did not die. God took him to heaven in a chariot of fire as explained in 2 Kings.[189]

"In the book of Malachi,[190] God tells us a similar event, similar to what occurred with John the Baptist at Jesus' first coming, will happen before the visual Catching Up,

---

[188] 1 Thessalonians 5:3
[189] 2 Kings 2:10-12
[190] Malachi 4:5-6

when Jesus arrives in the clouds at His second coming and the beginning of the Time of Jacob's Distress.

"The actual original Elijah will be sent back by God to provide another bold announcement that Jesus is about to return for a 'second time.' God will send Elijah to restore the *'hearts of the fathers to their children and the hearts of the children to the fathers.'* We are told this will happen *'before the coming of the great and terrible day of the Lord'* (*the Time of Jacob's Distress*). Elijah will bring Hebrew *'fathers (teachings of the prophets) and children (the Hebrews),'* together again, leading to the reestablishment of the 12 tribes of Israel. Elijah will then bring into being God's special 144,000 Jewish men for service to God inside the Time of Jacob's Distress, 'before' it begins.

"According to the Book of Revelation,[191] 144,000 Jewish converts to Jesus, the Messiah, will evangelize Jesus as the Jewish Messiah, they will say they are still Jews who believe, not referring to themselves as Christians. They will proclaim the Christ to the entire world through the full time of Jacob's distress — 12,000 from each of the 12 tribes of Israel. The 12 tribes need to be in place first.

"Prior to the Israel attack 1 ½ years ago, Israel didn't control the full extent of the physical geographic land areas promised to them by God. We've seen how God rectified this. God, in the days of Jacob, provided to each of his 12 sons (*the 12 tribes of Israel*) parcels of land, as of now a part of the new larger State of Israel, Israel proper today. In order to reestablish the tribal system God will need before He can collect the 144,000, the additional land mass needed to be a part of Israel. God reclaimed the land

[191] Revelation 7:4-8, *Stunned,* 2015, Blomgren, pages 82-86

Himself with His Ezekiel attack, '*From the river of Egypt as far as the great river, the river Euphrates.*' This, again as I mentioned before, is the land promised to Israel in Genesis[192] — the Abrahamic Covenant.

"Now in the Jewish faith at their Seder dinner they initially pour four cups of wine. Upon completion of the Seder celebration a fifth cup is poured referred to as 'the cup of Elijah.' The Jewish people look for Elijah to return. This fifth cup is taken to the front door and the door is opened. A prayer is offered asking G-d[193] to send Elijah to pour out wrath on their persecutors. They're thankful as they feel with this ceremony, the presence of Elijah graced them in spirit.

"Biblically per Malachi[194] God tells us He does intend to literally send Elijah back. When he literally arrives, this will stun Israel and set in motion all the things I told you about this event today. The prayer the Jews offered to G-d regarding Elijah for almost 2,000 years is about to be answered. A great blessing for G-d's chosen people … the Jews.

"Now let's go on to Event 23, the overwhelming Scourge, and the 11th Leader's proposed covenant with Israel.

"When this 23rd event, the overwhelming Scourge, begins to take shape, I will share more on this in Major Sermon #5. These events in prophecy 23 will indicate the Lord is at the door ready to open it. You will not want to miss Major Sermon #5.

---

[192] Genesis 15:18
[193] G-d Is how the Hebrews spell God out of respect.
[194] Malachi 4:5-6

"Prior to the start of the Time of Jacob's Distress, the main leader at the time,(the eleventh ruler we saw arrive will set a horrific army loose on the world starting around Israel,) the overwhelming scourge—as explained in the book of Joel.[195] Briefly,(demons will march in order and devour, burn, and destroy everything in their path.) They can go through windows into and over houses—terrifying to witness. The overwhelming scourge is a pivotal detailed warning sign possibly weeks prior to the visual Catching Up takes place.

"I believe this scourge will start to occur, heading for Israel from outside its borders first, while the people of the world still live in their perceived false peace and safety. The overwhelming scourge will terrify the world and due to proximity to the Holy Land will make Israel reluctantly desire to sign a covenant agreement [196] with the eleventh leader, who claims he can protect them from these horrible terrors. A grave error! [197] The actual covenant signing will start the official seven-year Time of Jacob's Distress. Informed Christians need not fear this horrendous scourge as this will arrive close to the day of our redemption.[198]

("The Bible indicates for us, in a set of verses in Luke,[199] the visual Catching Up and the start of the time of Jacob's distress must per historical precedent in Noah and Lot's days, happen within the same 24-hour day, with no time separation or gap between these two events.)God created

[195] Joel 2:1-10, *Stunned,* 2015, Blomgren, pages 197-204
[196] Isaiah 28:14-15
[197] Isaiah 28:18-19
[198] Joel 2:30-32, Like 21:25-28, 1 Thessalonians 4:13-18, *Stunned*, 2105, Blomgren, pages 188-192
[199] Luke 17:26-36

multiple important profound reasons for these two events to happen in this way. I will reveal these reasons in Major Sermon #5. (Through the Grace and the promises of God, true living believers in Jesus will escape[200] in a visual Catching Up event mere hours before a prominent world ruler signs his covenant with Israel, placing the Time of Jacob's Distress into motion.)

Over the next couple of years, John and I will present weekly sermons clarifying what is happening in the world as we see prophecies 21-23 transpire.

"I've now given you the 23 Biblical prophetic events God gave us in advance in the last days so we can believe,[201] so we're not caught by surprise regarding what He's doing related to His Son's return. We near the day the Lord will arrive in the clouds in a spectacular set of visual events that will be magnificent to behold. We are blessed.

"Dear, Lord, please continue to bless this church as we know that You are about to arrive. I know that what I am now sharing is not going to be received well by the world powers today, but I know You prepared me for this moment, to be sharing this before I was born. God please offer us all heavenly protection and allow me to share what we will soon see happening based on Your first 23 events. I look forward to the day I can share the grand finale prophecy 24 in Major Sermon #5. Please bless and keep everyone in Your family here on earth in your loving hands until Your glorious return. Amen.

Doc smiled ☺.

---

[200] The word escape is actually used in context by God Himself in the bible. Luke 21:36, 1 Thessalonians 5:3. The idea of escape is not wishful thinking it is real.
[201] John 14:29

†✿✿✿✿✿†

The last words of Allen Rogers' sermon faded from Guy Terrestre's penthouse office in the World Government building in Babylon. Below him Guy observed his new modern city spread out across the desert. Nearby stood the new One World Church Cathedral, simple in its design but impressive in scale.

All his plans were coming together, except the irritant of a minister from the former United States. In the past year and a half, Guy had moved into multiple positions of major power in the world, created a secret plan to take full charge of world government and religion. He'd almost arrived.

Even his closest aides knew nothing of his deepest, darkest plans. Yet Allen Rogers did, and he cautiously blasts those secrets out to the entire world. How could he know about the scourge, the coming of Elijah, how superficial the peace he planned for the world might become?

Yes, Terrestre would surprise the world to come. How could such a fringe group led by a nobody preacher who was the enemy of his new, powerful World Church know his plans? The Bible? That mess of nonsense? Yet he speaks the truth, Allen Rogers fully understands Guy's plans.

At least most of the world wasn't paying attention to Allen, not yet. With Guy's powers not completely consolidated, Terrestre knew a direct attack on this pastor at this time might be controversial and draw more attention to him. Better watch the situation. He said he's going to keep preaching every week from North America.

Terrestre gazed out the window at his growing empire. Let Rogers talk for now, don't mention him, ignore him. It's too early for Guy to show his hand, to give credence to what Allen Rogers says.

He was not at the point of putting an end to Allen's ministry ... yet.

11

PROPHECIES 21-23, UNFOLD

The day after Major Sermon #4, Guy Terrestre announced a major address to the world on Monday evening.

Allen tuned to the address, already aware in his own mind that Guy Terrestre was the prophesied eleventh leader to hold the world stage and had become the most powerful man in the world.

He waited with bemusement to hear the now so predictable words Terrestre used to calm the listeners.

Terrestre didn't disappoint. "My fellow citizens of Earth," he said. "Today peace and tranquility envelop our planet after many years of war and conflict. Enjoy life and prosper in the freest economy ever built. We the people of this world are now unified in our efforts to create a new world where conflict does not exist, where various peoples live side by side in comfort and peace, able to conduct their business anywhere on the planet with minimal disruption, where all of you are secure in your own homes and we've banished homelessness from the streets.

"There is nothing to fear. Follow all the desires of your heart, travel, work hard. I'm here to support you in all you want to accomplish and for the first time in history, you are totally free to do so.

"Full enlightenment exists here for the first time. Remember, we are all in this together."

"He's a mesmerizing speaker," Allen said to Joanne. "If I didn't know better, I might believe him. Most everyone will fall for his charisma and calming speech."

Joanne said, "You're mesmerizing as well, and your next Major Sermon will blow him out of the water."

Allen appreciated Joanne's faith in him then said, "A few more things need to happen before that sermon can go forward. Meanwhile the people of this planet play. They worship in the false church; they know not God."

"We're right in the middle of Event 21, the time of false peace and safety," Joanne said.

†✪✪✪✪✪†

Sam Gold met with Allen about four months after the fourth Major Sermon. "I believe we will be safe from Guy Terrestre and the Holy Babylonian Church until you decide the time is right for the next Major Sermon #5."

Allen said, "I'm already preparing it. I agree Terrestre is not ready to come after us yet. John and I are keeping our weekly messages until Major Sermon #5, to what we've already said so we don't stir up any more problems than we can handle.

"Right now, everyone is too caught up in the drama of the changed world they live in. It all seems wonderful to the untrained eye. We both know what can happen when a strong leader takes over then uses his power for hidden evil, which this man is doing."

"Are you certain you know who he is?"

Allen said, "For real? Yes, I'm afraid so. However, I will not mention his God-given title anywhere in this world until the fifth Major Sermon. The word is too dangerous."

Sam said, "The Holy Babylonian Church grew so large it includes almost everyone in the world. You saw how surviving Muslims flocked to join after Prophecy 13 devastated their world. The Pope turned into an exalted leader but Terrestre controls him now, as we knew he would. I don't know how many of Terrestre's people show up in our Sunday services, my guess is a lot. I'm sure they report back every word you say."

"I wouldn't want it any other way," Allen said. "They're paying attention to us even if they don't believe yet. Many will turn our way and join us in the Glory of God. The unbelievers are getting their last chance."

"For now, better for the secular world to think we are insane for not accepting the false good enveloping the world than for them to think our message is true."

†✧✧✧✧✧†

About six months after Major Sermon #4, Todd Proctor called Allen from Israel. Since the formation of the One World government, Todd often traveled to Israel under cover because most true intelligence flowed through the Mossad, the Israeli Intelligence service that also operated under cover, safe from discovery by Guy Terrestre.

"I'm coming back to Illinois in a few days," he said.

Allen hung up the phone with a feeling of surprise. Todd never acted so circumspect although phone calls seemed far more dangerous lately. Everyone knew the government officially monitored every call now.

Allen gave Todd a big hug when he arrived in Illinois. "Haven't seen you in a long time."

They went to the church, which was highly protected against bugs the Terrestre regime might want to plant, thanks to Sam Gold.

Allen closed the door to his office, they both sat down. "What's up?"

"You once told me the one event that might be hard to notice was number 22, the return of Elijah to the Jewish people. I think he's here."

"We always knew he might come back as a spiritual leader, like John the Baptist, to prepare the way for the Messiah. The Jews need this kind of guidance."

"This type of man appeared in Israel a few days ago. He is a humble, yet powerful man, well educated in the Torah. He is making inroads in the Israeli learned establishment. He's taken the name Elijah. I believe this is the arrival of Event 22. This man, in his first few days, is already beginning the task of rebuilding the 12 tribes of Israel as well as collecting 12,000 men from each of the new tribes, the 144,000 Jewish men dedicated to future service to God which must exist before the Catching Up."

Allen said, "Then the time is near."

†✡✡✡✡✡†

Twenty-three months after Major Sermon #4, Allen noticed Terrestre's rhetoric had become more extreme in recent weeks. Elijah, now well received in Israel, reestablished the 12 tribes of Israel so now every Jew knew which tribe they belonged to. Elijah taught his new group of 144,000 scholars the Old and New Testaments every Friday.

They fought Elijah on the study of the New Testament because they could not accept Jesus as the Messiah; but they respected Elijah and studied as directed. Israel built two venues for Elijah's men to hold all 144,000 at one time, an indoor arena, and an outdoor amphitheater. They switched from one to the other, weather permitting.

At this same twenty-three-month mark, almost two years to the day since Major Sermon #4, Allen waited eagerly for the event Doc told him to look for, the 23rd prophecy, the arrival of the scourge. This key sign would precede the return of Jesus by a short period, possibly weeks. He'd looked for signs of it for months, eager with anticipation, but nothing happened.

†✿✿✿✿✿†

Twenty-four months after Major Sermon #4, Sam Gold called Allen on a Monday morning with news. "It's begun," he said. "Terrestre is sending the scourge towards Israel. I've heard reports of a horrific army of demons who march in order and devour, burn, and destroy everything in their path. They go through windows into and over houses — terrifying to witness."

Allen said, "So the prophesied scourge begins.[202] Where do most of the reports come from?"

"The scourge is on the outskirts of Israel, about 10 miles outside the country on all sides, moving slowly, methodically towards the border and the Israelis know it. The press never mentions it, so most people live in their perceived false peace and safety. Nothing can stop it."

There was silence on the phone for a few moments.

"What else?" Allen asked.

("I hear, and it's rumor, the Israelis are scared to death. Guy Terrestre communicated with Israel's prime minister on the issue, met with him and gave Israel private assurances he can protect them from the scourge. He told them he would draft an agreement, a covenant, to protect them. Signing could be less than a month away.")

After Sam's call ended, Allen knew only a precious short time remained until event 24 arrived. The scourge also solidified his belief in Guy Terrestre's actual identity. Time for Major Sermon #5.

†✧✧✧✧✧†

The next Thursday night, the Prophecy Group met with all members in attendance.

Allen opened the meeting. "First, by the Grace of God, we are about to see the second arrival of Jesus Christ and the Catching Pp, the Rapture of His church. Guy Terrestre's vitriol against our church has reached a fevered pitch in recent days. It's like he's taken off the gloves and

---

[202] Joel 2

fights with the knowledge that his day to rule the world in full power is so near he can taste it.

It felt to the group like Guy Terrestre anticipated Allen would expose the next expected events in his next and final Major Sermon. Allen knew too much.

Allen said, "Next Sunday I'll present the final Fifth Major Sermon. With the 23 signs completed or ongoing and the arrival of the scourge we cannot wait any longer to make a final plea to the people of the Earth to accept Jesus Christ as their Lord and Savior.

"I've spoken with Doc, who appears to be busy these days. He supports me in taking these steps."

Sam Gold said, "I have a few items for the group. I believe Allen is right. The scourge we hoped for and prayed for has arrived.

"As you know, to oversee security I take care of problems before they arise. About four weeks back, John and I thought we might need a safe house for our group soon. Two of our parishioners, David Cooper and Fred Beshore, friends of John, offered us a lodge they own in a remote location. Their wives and children will join us at their refuge building. I set this facility up with provisions and our own generator and fuel so we could stay for up to three months as John and I felt that with the arrival of the scourge, this allowed enough time.)

"I can't tell you the location yet for obvious reasons, the fewer people who know the better. Over the last couple of weeks, I prepared this location as a final refuge. Bill Wright also stocked the refuge location with medical supplies we might need."

"What perfect timing," Allen said. "I've already talked with Sam and John about logistics. We can only take seventy people with us and I've already talked with each of you to create the list. We'll leave for this facility shortly after church this Sunday. Over the next couple of days, please pack essentials, bring your clothes, medications, toiletries, and minimal personal belongings to the church late Saturday night around 10:00 PM. Now to the plan for Sunday.

("On Sunday morning, 15 minutes before the end of church, please leave early to avoid traffic, drive to your homes, leave your cell phones and all your identification items, laptops and Commerce Purchase Cards in your homes, including your driver's license, wallet and purses, all locked inside your house. Also leave your One World Virus Free Clearance Cards in your homes as we are sure there are Global tracking devises built into every government card. Then drive back to Church. Plan to arrive at the church exactly two hours after the normal 10:30 AM completion time of our service, at 12:30 PM. The parking lot will be empty after everybody leaves. Prior to your 12:30 PM arrival at church, please grab a quick lunch.

"We'll park our cars in a prearranged area at the back of the church near our meeting hall, where two old busses will be parked. We'll all lock our car keys inside our cars as we will not need them any longer. We must leave for the refuge house quickly in our prearranged group transportation no later than 1:00 PM. We'll schedule a short meeting at the church before we depart. Nobody will pay any attention to the two old busses going on a church outing.")

Sunday morning Sam said, "We're all prepared. One key thing, Allen. I expect Guy Terrestre to make a major search for you. In your sermon, make a point to say you and John will be meeting on Wednesday morning at 8:00 AM to make final arrangements to close down the church. Terrestre might think we gave him a specific window of time to find us. He doesn't know we're planning to disappear. By the way, Fred owns the two busses I referred to. He parked them at the refuge for months so they will show up in current and older satellite images. We will use them as our transport to the retreat. Saturday night Fred and David, with their families, will drive the busses to church so they do not leave traceable vehicles here at our facility, giving our destination away. The busses will be refueled and parked inside our on-site warehouse and will not be seen Sunday morning. Terrestre's forces should not be aware of the bus movements."

"I agree," Allen said. "Anything we can do to distract him will help a lot. I want to be at the refuge before he starts looking for us. I hope when he shows up with his army, he'll find a bunch of empty cars and an empty church. I'm sure he'll scour our homes next week. I want him to find the phones and the identification to confuse him so he'll know we vanished. We'll be gone on Sunday. We know exactly what we need to do at the end of the sermon."

†✧✧✧✧✧†

Allen, John, Sam, Fred, and David's families stayed at the church the night before Major Sermon #5 after they brought their luggage and the two busses to the facility late Saturday night as planned. They left all their documents locked inside their homes Saturday evening. Fred and David left their cars at their homes, in their garages, totally off Guy's radar. They knew lots of tasks remained for Sunday morning and wanted to make sure everything went without a glitch after the service. Allen and John could not leave 15 minutes early as they needed to finish the sermon.

Sam said, "I made sure to scan the meeting room we will meet in Sunday after the service for any bugs and found none. I'll make sure everybody in the congregation leaves the campus after the service. Only the seventy of us will remain here in the meeting room at church so we can talk freely."

12

FINAL SERMON 5, PROPHECY 24

A DAY THAT WILL ALTER THE COURSE OF MANKIND

This Sunday, 3 ½ years after the attack, Allen's bold message stunned everyone. As usual, Allen opened in prayer:

"Dear Lord, open our eyes today, that we may behold wonderful things out of your law. In Jesus' precious name, Amen.[203]

"Good morning and welcome. This is the day the Lord has made; let us all rejoice as I believe with all my heart that what we saw last week indicates Jesus will return for us in a spectacular way now at any time. *Dear Lord, be with me and us today as I share what I now believe to be your incredible design for Jesus' spectacular visual second coming.*

"Today I bring you Major Sermon #5. This last in my series of five Major Sermons and it's the one I've waited to share all my life. Today I'm excited. I'll be blunt today as I

---

[203] Psalm 119:18

187

tell you how we can know the Lord's return will happen at any time now, possibly within weeks. All His 23 signs happened or started and are ongoing. I will soon share with you how I can make these coming categorical statements about event #24. I will also share why the Lord's return is now certain to happen but not in secret as Christianity has incorrectly assumed for hundreds of years. God tells us in prophecy that it is sure to happen; it will not be in secret. I'll show you today why Biblically God has multiple reasons for His arrival to be witnessed; seen by all of mankind, both Christians, Jews, and all remaining unbelievers. His arrival will set in motion another event that will formally start a seven-year period known in the Bible as the 70th week of Daniel; as explained in the book by the same name, Daniel.[204] This will be the literal Biblical seven-year Tribulation as described in detail in the book of Revelation.[205])

"Why do I keep talking about Daniel's 70 weeks? Because God loves the Jews, and so do I. Sixty-nine of the 70 weeks were completed per Daniel when 'the Messiah' was cut off. Jesus was cut off at the cross. Jesus is the Messiah. The Tribulation, the 70th week, will finally bring the Jews to acceptance of Jesus their Christ as their Messiah. The seven-year Tribulation that will soon arrive is targeted at the Jews and will be a time of great trials and tribulations (troubles) pointed directly at God's chosen people, again the Jews, with multiple purposes. Here is what the 70th week is designed to do for God's Glory,

---

[204] Daniel 9:24-27, *Stunned*, 2015, Blomgren, pages 78-81
[205] Jeremiah 30:7

Israel:[206] *'to finish all transgressions, make an end to sin, make atonement for iniquity, bring in everlasting righteousness, to put an end to visions and prophecy, and to anoint the most Holy City.'* All this is designed to complete and bring the Jews to the full acceptance and knowledge that Jesus the Christ is, and always was, their Messiah. What additional proof is there that 69 weeks already took place before the time of Christ's Crucifixion? Let's recap Daniel 9 for the answers.

"Cyrus gave a decree to rebuild Jerusalem and the second Temple.

"This began the 70 weeks of Daniel for God's chosen people.

"In God's accounting, each week is a period of seven-year timeframes, so this is how we know 70 weeks represents 490 years in total.

"Seven weeks are determined to rebuild the City and Temple (49 years).

"Sixty-two additional weeks will transpire until the Messiah is cut off or another 434 years. We believe the Messiah to be Jesus and He was cut off at the cross at year 483 of 490 years, seven years remain to happen, and must soon arrive to make things right between the Jews and the Christ for all eternity.

"Again, 69 weeks ended when Jesus the Christ, the Messiah, was cut off at Calvary so this means one week remains. Daniel tells us this will happen far off in the future, in the last days.[207] This is the 70th week of Daniel

---

[206] Daniel 9:24-27, *Stunned,* 2015, Blomgren, pages 78-81
[207] Daniel 9:24-27, *Stunned*, 2015, Blomgren, pages 78-81. Note the word "flood" in verse 26, is not literal. It represents a large overpowering army that will come to destroy the Temple. The Roman army. (It is not the flood of Noah.)

and it will arrive now at almost any moment. All prophecy is set. I know I'm being redundant here but this reality from the Tanakh is of vital importance for our Jewish family to understand. I want to implant this in them so they will take this to heart.

"Note again an important point: these 70 weeks are for His chosen people, the Jews. No Christian churches existed for the first 69 weeks. Logically we must then realistically assume the 70th week, one final seven-year period about to arrive, will be designed specifically for the Jews alone as well. Christians will be removed, 'caught up' first; but how? But why?

"Watch out for a widely accepted deception related to the timing of the Cyrus' decree. Evil forces in our world today do not want you to know certain truths in the last days.[208] Ptolemy was not correct in his widely accepted timing related to this decree occurring in 536 BC. We can know the exact year when the decree of Cyrus occurred, it is amazingly simple. Take Jesus' "the Messiah's" crucifixion date and subtract 483-years and you reach the correct date of the decree. It's simple if you accept the Bible and Jesus as the Messiah. I accept this simple math. God didn't want this to be complicated.

"In my first Major Sermon #1, 3 ½ years ago, the day of the Israel attack, I shared with you the 12 signs or end time prophecies God allowed the world to witness prior to that amazing day, starting in 1914. Prior to today, over these last 3 ½ years I provided four Major Sermons where I shared 11 more of God's 24 prophetic events, leading to what I told you many times will be a visual return of

---

[208] Ephesians 6:10-12

Christ. The added 11, as of last week with the arrival of the scourge, occurred, getting us through 23 of the 24 events, all confirmed. They all occurred for us to witness as God told us they would, and as I shared with you. There is one big event left, the third super sign in God's 24 event end times Road Map. The one I share today is multifaceted and will be incredibly spectacular!!!

"Here is how I know the Lord will come back within weeks. Remember, He gave us one of the key final signs we needed to watch for. Last week we saw the beginnings of the event in the 23rd prophecy from Major Sermon #4 out of Joel,[209] the arrival of the overwhelming scourge, now on the outskirts of Israel. As sparsely reported in the news, this terrifying event is starting to unsettle the world. As I have told you, believers are to be in the light[210] and are to know what this scourge is, why it is here and understand we do not need to be afraid of it. I'm not, I'm in awe!(This is a key sign that indicates God's grand finale for both Christians first and then the Jews seven years later is about to arrive;) Daniel's 70th week, the second of two parts in Prophecy 24.

"What I'm about to say now might surprise you and anger others but bear with me as I feel strongly God needs me to share this today. Jesus was and is to this day a Jew, the Messiah, our Jewish Savior. Remember, when we say Jesus Christ, this is not his first and last names. Christ in the Greek is Messiah, His title. A Christian is a person who believes in the Christ, the Jewish Messiah. Did you know the word Christian is used in the New Testament only 3

---

[209] Joel 2, the scourge, *Stunned*, 2015, Blomgren, pages 86-87, 198-199
[210] 1 Thessalonians 5:1-11, emphasis on verses 4-5

times? The word Jew is used 192 times.[211] Who might you think God is trying to talk to? All the apostles were Jews who never gave up their heritage; they are in heaven today as Jews who accepted Jesus as their Jewish Messiah. In the gospels Jesus tells the apostles to preach to the Jews first.[212] He then tells us the gentiles are now allowed to become believers and be accepted into the heavenly Kingdom to make His chosen people, the Jews, jealous.[213] We are commanded to help our natural Jewish family find Jesus as their true Messiah. They will hate us for attempting this as God told us they will, but we are commanded to do so, regardless.[214]

"What other evidence supports that God's story, to its conclusion in our time and near future, is about the Jews? When we get to the eternal order, the time after Jesus perfects everything for all eternity, God shares interesting information with us in Revelation 21.[215] God tells us about the eternal City of Jerusalem that comes out of heaven to earth, perfected, with 12 gates and 12 foundation stones. On each gate is written the name of one of the 12 Jewish tribes of Israel. Inscribed on each foundation stone is the name of one of the 12 Jewish apostles. For all eternity, when you go in or out of Jerusalem (God's most Holy JEWISH City) you will walk through a gate named for a Jewish tribe and over a foundation stone named for a Jewish apostle. This means that we will all live with God as our Father for all eternity in perfection, the law fulfilled

---

[211] This is true inside the New Testament
[212] Acts 13:5, 13, 42,46, 14:1, 17:1,17, 18:4-11, 19:8, 28:17, 28:28, *Stunned*,2015,
[213] Romans 11:11-16
[214] Luke 6:22, John 15:18, Romans 11:10-12
[215] Revelation 21:10-14

in a perfected Jewish society. All of us who believe in Jesus in this building today are adopted Jews and, when we receive our eternal bodies soon, will become perfected Jews. This will be glorious!

"Remember we are told in the gospels Jesus did not come to dismantle the Law but to fulfill it.[216] When we accept Christ the law is planted and perfected in our hearts through the blood of Christ. We are perfect in the eyes of God the Father fully unblemished, white as snow also through the blood of Christ.[217]

"All born again Christians[218] are about to go home with our Lord in a way far more majestic than we could ever comprehend. Here is what I believe the Bible literally says will arrive shortly for us at this moment in time. We will soon be with the Lord.

"Get ready for Event 24, the day the Lord will visually return for His church. This is the first of two parts in Event or prophecy 24.

"Again, we witnessed the beginning of the arrival of the overwhelming scourge as described to come in the last days in Joel 2.[219] This has multiple purposes related to what is about to come upon mankind. It is one of a couple of major final things to look for.

"This horror is controlled by our new eleventh world leader, who came to prominence on the world stage recently, Mr. Guy Terrestre. This statement is of the

---

[216] Matthew 5:17, Luke 24:44, Romans 8:3-5
[217] Isaiah 1:17-19
[218] John 3:3, John 3:7, 1 Peter 1:3, 1 Peter 1:23, *Stunned*, 2015, Blomgren, pages 265-281
[219] Joel 2, the scourge, *Stunned*, 2015, Blomgren, pages 86-87, 198-199

greatest importance since Guy Terrestre will soon be known as the real prophesied Antichrist!)

"This scourge event is already terrifying Israel. It is on their borders, coming towards them. No human power can stop it. They are terrified it may consume them.

"Mr. Terrestre will soon say, (for a price yet to be determined, he can prevent Israel from being affected by this scourge and I believe we will soon discover he is in the early stages of preparing a seven-year protection covenant[220] to be signed by Israel so this scourge will pass them by.) Wait and watch for this as it will be a final defining moment, the final sign of the arrival of prophecy 24, any day now.

("We know the scourge is the reason Israel will sign this covenant per the book of Isaiah, Psalm 83 and Daniel.[221] This will prove to be a grave error.[222])

"This agreement signing will start the 70th week of Daniel, as I talked about in detail many times, the Biblical seven-year Tribulation.

("Remember I mentioned earlier no Christians will remain on Earth on this single day when this event begins by God's incredible design.)

("We will be taken by Jesus mere hours before the signing in a specific way for significant reasons in a spectacular visual pre-Tribulation event.)

("You might say we cannot know the day or hour of the Lord's return and this is correct. But in Joel and Luke[223] we are told the day the Lord returns He will give us signs to

---

[220] Daniel 9:27
[221] Isaiah 28:14-15, Psalm 83:5, Daniel 9:24-27
[222] Isaiah 28:18-19, *Stunned*, 2015, Blomgren, pages 86-87
[223] Joel 2:30-32, Luke 21:25-28

show us literally the day when He will return mere hours before he arrives. He directs us to be in the light and to not be caught off guard and that His arrival this day should not be a surprise to us.[224])

"So, we will go to bed one evening not knowing that tomorrow will be the day of the Lord's return. (But when we see God's signs the next day, we will be assured the Lord will return this day. God offers a special reward for knowing this is true. This reward by Jesus is the Crown of Righteousness. [225])

"The Lord's return will come as a total surprise to the unbelieving world while they are living in a false time of peace as clearly described in the book of Luke.[226] Their world will be turned upside down. The unbelievers will be caught by surprise when their 'false peace' is stolen from them *like a thief in the night.*'[227] Informed Christians are to be in the light and to know exactly what is happening.[228]

"The Bible tells us when we see the final signs of the darkness, roaring of the seas, men fainting with fear for what they see is coming upon the world, an informed Christian is to prepare to lift up their head for their redemption is near.[229] Our Crown reward can only be received if we know when to *'look up.'* This is literal and for students of prophecy, God will give us a pre-warning

---

[224] 1 Thessalonians 5:1-11, emphasis verses 4-6

[225] 2 Timothy 4:8

[226] Luke 17:26-36

[227] 1 Thessalonians 5:1-11, emphasis verses 1-3, *Stunned*, 2015, Blomgren, pages 194-195

[228] 1 Thessalonians 5:1-11, emphasis verses 4-6, *Stunned*, 2015, Blomgren, pages 194-195

[229] Luke 21:25-28, *Stunned*, 2015, Blomgren, pages 197-204 – The *'look up'* command is literal, specific, detailed and incredible.

in our hearts, which I will share with you in a moment. This pre-warning will tell us the Rapture of the church is about to begin. Yes. A literal pre-Tribulation Rapture to be viewed by the entire world. I'm now going to tell you why. By the way I know the word Rapture is not used in the Bible, it is a modern word translated to represent the concept of being *'caught up'* to be with Jesus, which is literally in the Bible. [230]

"With the scourge first, then the signs of darkness in the world and then a shout from Jesus in the clouds, the visual Rapture event and finally the covenant signing with Guy Terrestre A.K.A. the Antichrist, will collectively be the most horrifying day in human history for those not Raptured, and it only gets worse.

"When Christians see these signs, if they follow prophecy, they know God tells us if we understand what He is doing and love His coming, we will receive the *'day star'* in our hearts.[231] This is the assurance from God that the Rapture is about to take place so we can know with certainty to *'look up'* to see our Lord return only in the clouds first at this time.

"The Rapture is an event where Jesus takes His bride the church to safety before He cleans things up on earth, bringing the Jews, His chosen family, to acceptance of Christ. He will be successful. This is like the story in the book of Ruth[232] where Boaz takes his new bride Ruth to safety while he cleans up family issues. As Boaz was Ruth's kinsman redeemer,[233] likewise Christ is ours and

---

[230] 1 Thessalonians 4:17

[231] 2 Peter 1:19, *'day star,'* King James version, for this translation.

[232] Entire book of Ruth

[233] Ruth 2:1-3, 3:1-3

will remove us from harm before He deals with His chosen people the Jews for seven years inside the 70th week of Daniel.)

"Now how do we know the Rapture will be a visual event and not in secret? Because seven stages occur in the Rapture as described in the Bible.[234]

"#1 = The wonders and signs that proceed prior to the Lord's return, as indicated in Joel and Luke.[235] We are to be the light[236] and are to know what these signs mean. The Lord says in 2 Peter He will give prophecy students who love His coming the *day star* in their hearts letting them know it is time to *look up,* per Luke.[237]

"#2 = The Lord descends from heaven with a shout.[238] I will address Isaiah 61:2 shortly regarding this shout; this shout from heaven is the second of three announcements assigned to be given by Jesus himself. He made the first when He was here originally, at His first teaching as a Rabbi in the synagogue. The third will occur at the end of the Tribulation.

"#3 = The sound of the first trumpet. Where there is a first there is usually a second.[239]

"#4 = The dead (bodies in graves described in the Bible as sleeping) in Christ rise first.(Those of us alive, who know what to do, haven't risen yet. Only living Christians who *look up* haven't risen into the sky yet. By the way, the whole world is seeing this happening, in real time.)I'll tell

[234] *Stunned*, 2015, Blomgren, pages 196-197
[235] Luke 21:25-26
[236] Luke 21:27-28
[237] 2 Peter 1:19, *day star,* King James version, for this translation.
[238] 1 Thessalonians 4:16, Isaiah 61:2b
[239] Matthew 24:30-32, 1 Thessalonians 4:16

you shortly what happens to(Christians who do not 'look up' because they didn't know what to do; they never studied prophecy. These people will pay a small penalty, but they will go up at the Rapture in a way described in 1 Thessalonians.[240])

"#5 = after the dead rise as the first group, and their souls are reunited with their resurrected earthly bodies, those of us looking up rise also into the sky as a second group in our earthly bodies alive to be with them.[241] None of us are changed into our eternal bodies yet.

"#6 = the world hears the final trumpet described in 1 Corinthians.[242]

"#7 = At this moment those of us in the air will all change, both groups, into our eternal bodies in a moment, the twinkling of an eye, at the last trumpet.[243]

"Why will God make the Rapture occur as a grand visual statement?

"Remember prophecy 22, the appearance of Elijah.

"Remember how I told you he would arrive per the book of Malachi[244] in the last days to bring the hearts of the fathers to the children and the hearts of the children to the fathers. This has happened. Elijah has reestablished the 12 tribes of Israel again after 2,000 years.

"With the re-established tribes. Elijah will bring 12,000 Jews from each of the 12 tribes, all serious Tanakh scholars the equal of Saul the pharisee/Paul to be formed for a

---

[240] 1 Thessalonians 4:13-18

[241] 1 Thessalonians 4:13-18, emphasis on verse 16-17

[242] 1 Corinthians 15:52

[243] 1 Corinthians 15:51-52, we are all change in the seventh event after the "last trumpet." The Rapture cannot be a secret, surprise event.

[244] Malachi 4:5-6

great purpose, 144,000 men total. This also happened for those who watch the news.

"As with Paul, God would not allow him to be converted until the right moment. After Christ ascended into heaven, Jesus in spirit arrived on a road to Damascus and converted Saul, the killer of Christians, in a bright light. He became Paul, the greatest of all apostles for Christ.

"God will not allow these 144,000 men to accept Jesus until a specific moment in time for a purpose. They need to be ready for God's service on day one of the Tribulation. The Rapture will play a major role related to the 144,000.

"Additionally, all our friends we shared the good news with who did not accept Christ prior to the day of the Rapture will experience another insight of great importance, they will know we're right.

"Remember, I told you living Christians who 'look up' and those who don't will experience the Rapture differently. The Bible says in the last days those who desire to save their lives will lose them and those who are willing to lose their lives will save them.[245] (God told us to take a specific action, literal about the Catching Up, the Rapture and if we do not do as He says there is a small consequence.) Therefore, God tells us to remember Lot's wife.[246] She was told not to look back when God destroyed Sodom. She did look back and her consequence ... she turned into a pillar of salt. She went to heaven, but she went the hard way. God tells us a similar warning, when

---

[245] Luke 17:32-36, *Stunned*, 2015, Blomgren, pages 212-216
[246] Luke 17:32-33, *Stunned*, 2015, Blomgren, pages 178-180, alternate paths for living Christians in the Rapture, pages 213-216

we see the terrors of all His last day signs, if we know to 'look up,' we go alive into the sky. If due to lack of knowledge and fear a Christian goes to hide, God will put them to death just prior to the first trumpet and they will go up with the dead, the first group. They won't know this happened until they find out in heaven, they missed out on their final open book test and do not get their crown for not knowing what to do.

"Now let's address an important item from the book of Isaiah 61:1-2. Through a prophetic literary tool of impersonation, Isaiah makes a pronouncement plus three announcements regarding what the Messiah will claim or say in their future. It is written this way so in the future the Messiah Himself, Jesus, can quote this prophecy directly, claiming credit as the One authorized to say it. The Messiah is granted the authority in Isaiah 61:2 to announce all three things; the first is the *favorable year of the Lord*, the second the *day of vengeance of our God*, and the third a time to *comfort those who mourn*. How do we know Jesus is the One appointed to make these three announcements? God tells us in Luke.[247]

"Jesus makes His first appearance as a Rabbi in the Synagogue and does the reading this day; this reading is the same in all synagogues this Sabbath day, which is Isaiah 61.

"He reads this passage as if it is Him pronouncing the words and stops after He announces *the favorable year of the Lord* and sits down.[248] The crowd is stunned. He does not make the second and third announcements, but why?

---

[247] Luke 4:14-22
[248] Luke 4:20

"*The favorable year of the Lord* is the long period from His first visit until He returns at the Rapture.

"Then to the stunned crowd He announced *that today this pronouncement is fulfilled in their hearing.*[249]

("IMPORTANT: Jesus will make the second announcement, announcing *the day of vengeance of our God,*[250] in the shout from the clouds. This announces the arrival of the Tribulation, which will trigger the Rapture, which happens mere hours before the signing of the covenant officially starting the Tribulation.)

"The third announcement will be at the start of the Millennium at the end of the Tribulation.

"All three announcements are to be made by Christ Himself at different times.

"Why is this all so important? Again, God offers a crown reward in heaven[251],[252] for loving His coming and knowing what to do and when to '*look up*' as explained in Luke and Revelation.[253]

"Only those still living at the Rapture can possibly go up alive and obtain this crown without dying first. God especially blessed those of us alive today as we will see this while living. The dead who go first, those who loved His coming, will also get this crown.)

"Finally, there is something everyone needs to know about the Tribulation. Many churches today will tell you if there is a tribulation period, (it will be peaceful for the

---

[249] Luke 4:21

[250] Isaiah 61:2b second announcement of 3, *"the day of vengeance of our God."*

[251] 2 Timothy 4:8, Crown of Righteousness for those looking for the Lords' return. God offers 5 crowns in life, see *Stunned,* 2015 Blomgren, pages 216-218

[252] Revelation 3:10-11, do not let anyone take your crown 'false church?"

[253] Luke 21:25-28, *Stunned*, 2015, Blomgren, pages 197-204

first 3 ½ years. This is categorically incorrect! But why? The book of (Revelation tells us inside the seven-year Tribulation there will be 21 judgments. In the first half there are the seven Seal judgments and the seven Trumpets judgements, 14 in total. In the last half the seven Bowls. In Seal #4,[254] ¼ of those alive inside the Tribulation will die. In trumpet judgment #6,[255] another 1/3 of those remaining will also die. Let's do some simple math: start with the number 1,000 remove ¼ and you have 750 remaining, then now remove another 1/3 and you now have 500 or half of the original number. These two events will mean half of those living in the world left after the Rapture is completed will die in the first 42 months[256] or 1,260 days[257] or 3 ½ years of the Tribulation. To put this in perspective, let's assume six billion people remain on earth after the Rapture is completed this would mean three billion people will die in the first 1,260 days. Doing some simple math again this comes out to 2,380,000 people on average PER DAY! Statistical research shows that today in our world about 160,000 people die per day out of a population of close to 8 billion. Compare this to the number of people who died in the Virus worldwide over a year. And we all thought the Virus was bad.

As you can deduce, no peace of any kind will occur inside the Tribulation. No rational person should ever desire to enter this period, God offers a way to escape[258]

---

[254] Revelation 6:8
[255] Revelation 9:18
[256] Revelation 11:2
[257] Revelation 11:3
[258] Joel 2:32, Luke 21:36, 1 Thessalonians 5:3

through Christ. Do not be deceived. Escape is God's word not mine.

"I know what I shared today will be mocked and criticized but I cannot tell you how strongly I believe this is what is about to occur including why. Remember this, in these final days, do not follow the herd mentality if they stray from Jesus. Know that when we get to Heaven we are not in a group when we face God. He deals with us one-on-one. By accepting Jesus when we stand before God, Jesus intervenes for us and we are fully pardoned. I implore all here in attendance and in the television audience who have yet to choose Jesus, time is short to make a wise eternal choice.

"As you all know, with the help of the Holy Spirit I shared with you 23 end-time prophetic events, directly out of the Bible. All came true as God told us they would. Please seriously consider that what I shared with you today about the final 24th event will also occur as described. We can trust God on His accuracy.

"I've given you the best wise instruction I can offer so you can prepare for what will come now at any day. We are at the finish line for the sixth church of Philadelphia as described in the book of Revelation.[259]

"In conclusion today, to all my Jewish family and all those who have yet to seriously consider accepting Jesus as your personal Savior, I have a final heartfelt passionate plea; please seriously consider a decision for Jesus Christ the Messiah soon, time is running short. In the book of John[260] God tells us *'For God so loved the world, that He gave*

---

[259] For the Church of Philadelphia see page 124-125 in this book.
[260] John 3:16

His only begotten Son, that whoever believes in Him shall not perish, but have eternal life.'

"Then we are also told in the book of John[261] that one needs a *'born again'* conversion acknowledging belief in the Lord. *'Jesus answered and said to him, 'Truly, truly, I say to you, unless one is born again, he cannot see the kingdom of God.'*

"In the book of Matthew[262] God told us only a few are going to make it into the Heavenly Kingdom. *'Enter through the narrow gate; for the gate is wide and the way is broad that leads to destruction, and there are many who enter through it. For the gate is small and the way is narrow that leads to life, and there are few who find it.'*

"God gives us a serious warning about our world and how we live our lives, admonishing us to be careful in the book of 1 John[263]: *'Do not love the world nor the things in the world. If anyone loves the world, the love of the Father is not in him. For all that is in the world, the lust of the flesh and the lust of the eyes and the boastful pride of life, is not from the Father, but is from the world. The world is passing away, and its lusts; but the one who does the will of God lives forever.'*

"Pascal's wager comes to mind. Blaise Pascal (*1623–1661*)—a French philosopher, scientist, mathematician, and probability theorist—offered a profoundly simplistic viewpoint. I have paraphrased his thoughts for you as follows: *'If there is no God and we believed in Him; we have lost nothing. But if there truly is a God and we do not choose to believe in Him, we have a great deal to lose.'*

"With a contrite and humble heart, accepting the Lord is very simple, Jesus our Messiah made this easy to do as

---

[261] John 3:3
[262] Matthew 7:13-14
[263] 1 John 2:15-17

described in the book of Romans[264]: '... *if you confess with your mouth Jesus as Lord, and believe in your heart that God raised Him from the dead, you will be saved; for with the heart a person believes, resulting in righteousness, and with the mouth he confesses, resulting in salvation. For the Scripture says, whoever believes in Him will not be disappointed. For there is no distinction between Jew and Greek; for the same Lord is Lord of all, abounding in riches for all who call on Him; for Whoever will call on the name of the Lord will be saved.'*

"Once a person has accepted the Lord, this person's salvation is fully secured for all eternity as God also tells us in the book of Romans[265]: '*For I am convinced that neither death, nor life, nor angels, nor principalities, nor things present, nor things to come, nor powers, nor height, nor depth, nor any other created thing, will be able to separate us from the love of God, which is in Christ Jesus our Lord.'*

"Christianity is like a marriage proposal by Jesus to our souls . . . a very intimate thing. We can accept His proposal only prior to our physical death in this world. We can accept Jesus only until our last breath in this life. Because unexpected events might occur in our lives each day and with longevity unknown, this decision should not be taken lightly. At risk is eternal life with God, or eternal separation from Him ... Hell!

"The 7-year Tribulation is about to arrive with fury, it will be horrific. I would not wish this period on my worst enemies. Every Jew and non-believer that hears my words today, you have until you see the signs in the sun, stars, and earth that God will soon bring to make your peace and

---

[264] Romans 10:9-13
[265] Romans 8-38-39

accept Jesus. If you wait too long you will enter the Tribulation. Please seriously consider a wise choice.

"It is with a sense of sadness, yet great expectation, that John and I will not be giving additional sermons after today. This is the last sermon to be preached from this pulpit. The lights will go out on the Kingdom Today Center as of Wednesday noon, when John and I will officially close this facility. I've equipped all of you with what you need to know for our last days here on Earth. I've completed my public service for the Lord. With the arrival of the scourge last week the Lord knocks at the door.

"Wait now for a final announcement from Guy Terrestre regarding the day of the signing of a Covenant with Israel. I strongly believe the day this signing takes place is the day we'll see God's final signs, receive the 'day star' in our hearts, 'look up' and go home with our Lord and Savior for all eternity.

"I believe with confidence from the Holy Spirit the next time I see many of you will be when we are with our Lord in His heavenly Kingdom. This day will be glorious!

"Now may the God of Abraham Isaac and Jacob be with you all as we prepare for the arrival of the King of kings and Lord of lords, our beloved Savior, our Messiah Jesus the Christ. Come quickly Lord Jesus … Amen, Amen and Amen."

And … Doc smiled ☺.

13

GLORIOUS EVENT 24 ARRIVES

THE ENTIRE WORLD IS STUNNED!

Right after the sermon, Doc came up on stage. "You gave a magnificent closing sermon, "he said.

"Thank you. It means a lot that you think so," Allen said.

Doc said, "I wanted to let you know I need to leave as I have an important final assignment that I need to prepare for. The Lord is coming soon so I'll do my best to meet up with the group before He returns."

Allen watched him walk up the aisle with a sense of gratitude and joy.

Half an hour after Major Sermon #5 Allen, Joanne, John, and Alice walked into the church facilities meeting hall. To their great surprise, they found the entire group with all their family members present, ready for the escape to the secret secure location. A cheer went up when Allen entered the room.

A man in the group stepped up to Allen. "We arranged it all with Sam," he said. "We're so excited, we couldn't wait. Together we decided as a group to lock up our homes before coming to church, brought sack lunches with us. Why wait, we're ready to go now. Sam even coned off a parking area near the meeting hall last night, so all our cars were in the correct location this morning."

Allen hugged the man, then stood up on a chair to speak.

"What a surprise! I'm glad you're all here so we can leave quickly at just the right moment. We need to wait for the parking lot to clear out then we can get a fast start. My friends, today is an exciting day for us as we now know we will be with Jesus Christ shortly. One more check, did everyone leave your cell phones, computers, One World Virus Free Status Card and Commerce Purchase Card at home? We need to vanish without a trace. Your cars will stay where you parked them. Sam, did you count everyone here?"

"All seventy accounted for," Sam said.

"We'll leave our cars at the church with the keys locked inside. If Guy's minions show up this week, they won't know what happened. They will know from the registrations who's missing but won't be able to find us, we literally vanished. The busses are fully fueled, loaded and ready to go."

Allen paused. The group looked up expectantly. He wiped a tear away from his cheek. "I am so sad that the secular world believed Guy Terrestre's lies. I did my best to counter those lies."

He gazed at the silent crowd. How could so many people think they lived in a strong time of worldwide peace and harmony? How could they ignore the reality of evil, not pay attention to the daily norms of rampant decadence, to the crime, murders, sexual assaults, attacks and heavy hatred of the Jews, marginalization of true believers in the Bible and in Christ? "The world was so blind," he said.

He thought back to the attacks on him. Sad that the world considered true Christians the evil people in this age. In Isaiah[266] God said, *"Woe to those who call evil good, and good evil..."* This attitude became rampant, a Biblical sign of the times.

Allen said to the group, "We've almost finished our work here. I never understood when I started this church so many years ago that I would preach Biblical prophecies to such a huge audience. I also never guessed life as a prophecy teacher could be so perilous as the end of the age arrived.

"Only one prophecy is left. 23 of God's 24 end-time prophecies are complete or in play, time is exceptionally short."

Allen stood in silence for a moment, then said, "Let us pray." He repeated the prayer he used in all his sermons for the last 3 ½ years, words he found beautiful and necessary.

"Dear Lord, open our eyes today, that we may behold wonderful things out of your law. In Jesus' precious name, Amen. [267]*"*

He allowed a minute of silence while the group contemplated the meaning of the prayer and their nearly completed journey. Allen realized for the first time this

---

[266] Isaiah 5:20-21
[267] Psalm 119:18

verse asks the Lord to open our eyes so that we may behold … 'see' wonderful things out of His law … 'prophecies'. How profound, God has been telling us all-along in Palms 119 to pray so we can see all His 24 prophecies arrive. He never saw this before today. God is amazing!

"Three and one-half years ago, we began this new ministry," he said. "We've achieved incredible results. Today we give all praise and glory to God for the opportunity to share His plans for the last days with so many, so honestly and boldly.

"We started 38 years ago with a few hundred people. In the years since we reached a high level of accomplishment for the Lord. Right after the service today I heard the ratings for today's sermon reached the highest point ever, almost 55,000 in attendance, including adjacent meeting halls and courtyards, and over 200 million television viewers worldwide for my final sermon this morning.

"I guessed Guy Terrestre was the Antichrist after the completion of Major Sermon #3. I wanted to be shrewd as I needed confirmation from God. This is God's story, not mine. When the scourge arrived last week and we heard Guy started to prepare an agreement with Israel to protect them from the scourge, we received full confirmation of Guy's actual identity. Now we wait for the Lord to arrive."

Allen stepped down off the chair, motioned to John and Sam to join him in a corner away from the crowd.

John said, "It's clear the decision to announce to the world the end of our ministry was wise."

Allen said, "I knew this 5th Major Sermon would raise eyebrows and ruffle feathers and knew we might need to go into hiding. I know what it means to be shrewd as a serpent and innocent as doves."[268]

John said, "Good news. The full story is out and is a major news event trending worldwide. Our sources in Babylon say they have never seen a man so irritated as Guy Terrestre after your sermon today. You both saw how much he hated what Allen did in previous sermons, the sermon today was of-the-charts."

Allen said, "Let's be clear about the opponent we face. My opinions do not match Guy Terrestre's rosy view of this world. Most of the secular world doesn't know he's creating a deception. They think he's a great man who tells the world what I said about him was blasphemy. The blinded world is about to find out how evil he is. I'm certain his police force will swarm the church on Wednesday at the latest looking for us. Wise bait to make the announcement we would be here Wednesday between 8 a.m. and noon."

John said, "Having said all that, this is why we need to protect ourselves until the Rapture comes."

"Which will be in a short time," Allen said. "The completion of 23 of the 24 prophecies and the arrival of the scourge leaves no room for doubt on timing. All we need now is the announcement from Guy Terrestre assigning a date to sign the prophesied covenant agreement with Israel to protect the Jewish State from the scourge,[269] which is currently increasing in intensity and beginning to

---

[268] Matthew 10:16
[269] Daniel 9:27

frighten the whole world. The world's false peace is starting to crumble.

"Sam confirmed the church campus is empty. Everyone is gone. Let's get everyone on those busses and get out of here right on time."

✿✿✿†✿✿✿

After Allen's group left on their bus trip to their secure location, they had no contact with the outside world so didn't hear about events in Babylon. About the same time the group left on the busses, two hours after Allen finished Major Sermon #5, a bulletin went out announcing to the world that Guy Terrestre would go on the air in thirty minutes. The world had no idea he was livid.

Thirty-minutes later, the television announcer switched to the penthouse office Guy Terrestre built for himself overlooking the grand City of Babylon. Terrestre sat at his desk, stared into the camera, smiled at his worldwide audience.

He leaned forward, aimed his hypnotic eyes straight at his admirers. "Fellow citizens of Earth," he said. "Today we look forward to a new and grand future for this planet. In the last few years, I created paradise here on the earth. Crime is at a new low, people feel secure in their lives, we've eliminated the threat of international war. All these accomplishments happened in a few short years under my leadership. We can be proud of what I built for you.

"Yet one group opposes us. The so-called Christians are not strong, most of you ignore them. They teach an impossible mishmash of prophecies which can never come true, regardless of what they say.

"They are an irritant, too many oppose me, call me names, make bogus accusations, when all I want to do is bring peace to earth for the first time in history. You will see shortly how evil their intentions are. They are a menace; they want to undo all the good I've accomplished. Where they got all those lies, I cannot fathom."

Terrestre's voice boomed out of the television. "We must eliminate this menace to our plans. We cannot allow opposition. Look at where you stand. You are either with us or against us. If you are against us, you will fail. They are the evil people in our world today. I will soon make sure they are no longer able to spread their lies.

"Let's all keep the peace and prosperity we enjoy for millennia to come. I will never let you down." His image vanished from the screen.

✿✿✿✝✿✿✿

All members of the group arrived at the retreat in the forest ten miles outside the village of Wisconsin Dells Sunday afternoon about 7:00 PM. They all settled in, unloaded, and assembled in the resort's meeting hall for a late dinner.

After dinner, Allen gathered them around him, no microphone, no television cameras, no formal stage, only a crowd of fervent believers, family, and friends ready for God's next steps.

"It is great to be close to the return of Christ and safe here in our retreat." Allen said. "We've come on a long journey and the end is now near. We all need to be ready for the final days, so I'll go over in detail again what we need to watch for. In one word, it's up to Guy Terrestre now. Our hosts at this retreat set up a private cable television news feed for us that Terrestre cannot break into so we can follow events on the outside."

As Allen talked, Fred approached him, whispered into his ear. He paused, looked slightly worried, then smiled. "Fred tells me that while we rode the busses to our secret location here in the Dells, Guy Terrestre made a worldwide statement directed at us. Fred recorded the statement so let's look at it."

Allen watched with trepidation. He knew how smooth Terrestre's words could sound, how he carefully fashioned the menace he wanted to convey to one listener, Allen Rogers, and his ministry.

"He knows we reached over 200 million people with my message today on television. Can you sense his fear of God's truths being revealed?"

John said, "He can do a lot of damage to us."

"That's why we needed to protect ourselves. God also had a large hand in our protection."

Joanne said, "It's a brilliant move to shut down the ministry. We can't be a target anymore."

"Looks like we crossed his red line," Allen said. "This message wasn't meant for the world, it's meant for us, to scare us into silence. God wanted us to mess up his plans and we did our job. We're almost finished now. We must remain steadfast in God's eyes."

John said, "I can tell he's finished with us, ready to take us out. He thinks few people accept our teachings. We know millions do and we know he's angry. He'll never contain us, ever."

"Let's get on with our plans," Joanne said.

"Now that we put this Sunday announcement by Guy Terrestre behind us," Allen said, "a few more things need to happen before the seven-stage visual Rapture event begins, all integral parts of the 24th prophecy. All these events will happen before the signing of the covenant between Guy Terrestre and Israel to protect them from the scourge. This covenant signing starts the Tribulation.

"We know the Rapture must happen on the same day Israel and Terrestre sign the covenant. Both events occur in one day for major reasons.[270]

"Our plan is for all of us to be together when this comes true for this magnificent God moment.

"God instilled this blessing on our entire group and all Christians in the world who understand what we shared with them regarding what God teaches us through His gift of prophecy: The ability to know approximately what to look for so we can share together His return with friends and loved ones. God does not intend for the Rapture to be a lonely secret experience but a joyful visual group event for those alive when it happens. The next step is to wait for Guy Terrestre to announce the day he plans to sign his covenant agreement with Israel, so we wait."

After a long Sunday, everybody retired for the night.

✿✿✿†✿✿✿

---

[270] Luke 17:26-26, *Stunned*, 2015, Blomgren, pages 204-207

To everyone's surprise, the anticipated announcement regarding the covenant signing arrived quicker than Allen expected. The next day, Monday morning, Guy Terrestre held a press conference. John, Allen, and the rest of the core group sat around the satellite television in the main hall to listen.

Terrestre appeared on the screen with two delegates from Israel for the announcement. "In two weeks, on Friday, I will sign a historic covenant, a seven-year deal, with the State of Israel to protect them from the scourge. This will allow Israel to celebrate this great protection agreement on Saturday, their Sabbath.

"One other announcement. The radical heretic preacher Allen Rogers closed his church. Early on Monday morning, I raided his facility to close him down forever and arrest him. It appears he fled with a few of his cohorts. We've occupied the church facility and seized all the records available there, including electronic records and so forth, not much was left. We are at their homes now. You will never hear him preach his nonsense again. They were very shrewd regarding their departure, but we expect to capture them within a few weeks.

Terrestre went off the air. Allen stood and faced the group. "Good thing we left quickly yesterday; Guy doesn't care much for us. Today's announcement of the signing of the Covenant is the final event we've waited for, the final prophetic indicator the Rapture will likely occur in two weeks on the same Friday the covenant is signed."

Later, the group assembled in the meeting hall. Allen as usual led the meeting.

"Now that the covenant is being signed, we need only two more signs from God to confirm the Rapture will occur Friday after next: God providing signs in the sun and stars and on the earth[271] and the *'day star'* [272] arising in our hearts. These two events give us confirmation from God that the Rapture is about to begin so we can know to literally *'look up.'*[273] We are to know the season[274] of the Lord's return derived from prophecy but until we see these final signs and the *'day star'* arrives in our hearts, we will not know for certain."[275]

John stood and said, "I think I speak for everyone when I wish Doc could be here with us, but he mentioned he has an important final assignment to prepare for and plans to join us soon as possible. I hope he can make it and be with us at the Rapture"

Allen said, "I can't understand why Doc would now, at this incredible moment, choose not to be with us since he's our greatest supporter and guide for the last 3½ years. I keep remembering his mysterious arrival the day of the attack on Israel. This comforts me that he will find a way. Doc's my greatest supporter for 42 years since we first met.

"Dear God, I hope Doc can make it because it would be a great blessing and would mean a lot to us all."

✿✿✿†✿✿✿

Friday, a beautiful tranquil, sunny, cloudless morning, the actual prophesied day of the covenant signing, arrived

---

[271] Luke 2:31
[272] 2 Peter 1:19, *'day star,'* King James version, for this translation.
[273] Luke 21:28
[274] Luke 12:54-56
[275] Luke 21:25-28, with emphasis on verse 28

at the Wisconsin Dells resort. Allen felt a strong sense of anticipation with great excitement from the group. Where was Doc? Allen hoped he could make it; time was running short. Funny he never asked where we were going" How will he possibly find the group?

The isolation of their private lodge, miles from anywhere, kept them safe. They needed the extreme isolation because in the aftermath of Major Sermon #5, they knew Guy Terrestre sent out search parties for them. Good that they vanished. Allen silently thanked Sam Gold for setting up the retreat so quickly along with all the precautions that kept it and the group from detection.

But where was Doc? The quiet of this morning felt deafening.

✿✿✿✝✿✿✿

Allen heard the knock on the front door of the private lodge first. "John, come here!" he called out. Many others in the group became concerned and hid in the far corners of the large meeting hall.

Was this knock a sign Guy's minions found them?

John walked into the entrance hall.

"A knock on the door," Allen said. "Did they find us?"

"You know the precautions," John said. "They couldn't possibly find us. We left everything at home. All we have is satellite television provided by Fred Beshore and David Cooper and they are not on Guy's radar, so we're safe, they can't track us."

John walked to the door, pulled it open with great confidence.

Doc! Everyone in the room gave a joyful gasp.

Allen stared. Nobody told Doc where we were. How did he find us? This is a joyous moment!

The group's only connection with the outside world came through their satellite television tuned to the One World News Network (OWNN), which they watched with anticipation for certain worldwide events this day. The television remained on, but Allen placed it on mute when Doc arrived.

Doc entered, surveyed the crowd surrounding him, said, "It is my humble honor to greet all of you who did God's work in such a spectacular manner. Please join me in the main meeting room because I possess information of great importance to share with you from the Friend who detained me for the last two weeks since Allen's final sermon."

After five minutes of rustling about, everyone sat in the room with great anticipation.

Doc stood, faced the group, and raised a hand for silence. At that moment Allen, and the whole group, felt a rumbling motion, followed by a sharp earthquake that seemed destined to get their attention but not damage the facility.

At the same time, the clear morning sky darkened, a severe wind started to roar past the building. Allen wondered how this happened at the instant Doc arrived to talk with them.

"Allen, please join me in front of the crowd," he said in a soft voice.

Allen joined him. He felt unsure at the attention he was getting.

Doc began to speak. "Allen, 45 years ago, I was assigned to come and visit a young seminary student at a party. He didn't know it at the time, but he was destined to become a great honest man for God, preaching prophetic truth at a critical time in the last days.

"I was assigned to teach Biblical prophecy at this time, but my true assignment was you.

"For almost five years I taught you and you listened, learned as God prepared you for the moment that occurred the day Israel was attacked 3½ years ago. He assigned me to come back to you then for support and encouragement during your five Major Sermons.

"Your direction for your early ministry, the path you chose, created one of the largest church audiences in the world in the last days. Your original vision gave you a massive platform from which to teach the truth you always desired to share with the world at the right moment in history. God knew this would happen all along.

"We didn't talk for over 35 years, until the attack on Israel, not because I desired to not be with you, but because my Friend, our Heavenly Father, told me you needed time to work your ministry out through free will. Our Father gave me a new assignment during this time gap.

"The earthquake you all felt, and the following darkness are the beginning of the signs God shared with mankind for this day in history. The entire world is experiencing this at the same time including the following things about to rapidly arrive: [276]

---

[276] Luke 21:25-28, Joel 2:30-31, Joel 2:1-2

"Wonders in the sky and earth.

"Blood, fire and columns of smoke. The sun will go dark on the day side of the world.

"The moon will turn to blood on the dark side of the world.

"Dismay will occur among all the nations today.

"The seas will roar.

"Men all over the world will tremble in fear for what they sense is coming on the world.

"The power of the heavens will be shaken.

"Today will be a day of darkness and gloom for the unbeliever world.

"With all these signs happening, not one person on earth will sleep. Terror arrived.

"The Lord will return this day, and the Tribulation will then quickly start ... today.

"The Tribulation is designed to last for seven years and it will get progressively worse.

"The world's false peace and safety is being stolen away at this moment.

"All hell is about to break out on the earth this day."

Everyone glanced up at the television, Allen briefly turned off the mute to see an Alert Bulletin which reported a worldwide earthquake, confirmed this never occurred in the world before, the entire world became dark and ominous quickly, verification for the group that the day of Christ's return arrived. The mute button went back on.

Allen said, "Doc, you stated all these things with a sense of power and of full authority. I've never seen you like this. How is this possible?"

A sudden bright glow appeared around Doc's head like a halo. His clothing transformed to a bright white robe. He stood in a full bright light, stunned Allen and everyone else!

Doc raised his hand to quiet the group. "I'm the guardian angel appointed to guide Allen toward his free will destiny to serve boldly for God during the last days, sharing with the world what God is doing through prophecy and to share with the world the return of His Son will be visual, not in secret for all the reasons you taught your congregation in your five Major Sermons. The church of the last days has weakened to the point of impotence, arrogance and pride. [277] Mankind, self-serving, assumes God is all about affirmation of anything they desire to do, not understanding the Lord is a God of transformation, bringing individuals closer to Holiness, being more like Jesus. Today, the vast majority accept that what is right is wrong and what is wrong is right from a Biblical perspective.[278] God this day will start to set things on the correct course once and for all. Foolishness is about to meet its end.

"God knew you, Allen, would become the man you turned out to be. He is well pleased. Well done, good and faithful servant.[279]

"True prophecy-believing Christians in the whole world, who love His coming with anticipation, now know what the signs they are seeing mean and will know to *'look up'* at a specific moment as God directs. All these special

---

[277] Revelation 3:14-17
[278] Isaiah 5:20-21
[279] Matthew 25:21, 23. Luke 19:17

believers will soon be given the *'day star'* in their hearts, the assurance by God that the Rapture, the return of Christ in the first of two events He will perform over a seven-year period is near. His first arrival in the clouds is about to come within minutes in a way far more spectacular than ever thought possible. I can confirm now you and your entire group will get the *'day star'* assurance shortly. Then the signs of the Lord's return will grow in intensity, the Rapture will occur followed almost immediately by the start of the Tribulation. The time to *'look up'* to receive your crown for knowing what to do and when at this moment, is at hand.

"It is time now for me to leave you. My work here is completed. God bless you Allen and your entire group. We will all meet again in God's heavenly kingdom … this day."

Doc vanished in a bright light; the entire group felt incredibly blessed, filled with tremendous joy and pure wonder.

The group in the lodge with Allen, who witnessed Doc's reveal, represented a small group including extended families, children, and grandchildren, again in total 70 people.

The signs of the Lord's return they studied in detail arrived this day and intensified. The group watched their only human connection to the outside world, the television. All channels reported alerts as most of the events and signs prophesied to arrive prior to the Lord's return, everything Doc shared with them, started to happen worldwide.

Rick A. Blomgren

✿✿✿†✿✿✿

Outside in the secular world, news reports flowed in. The unusual events terrified the people of the world. The events rolled in, catastrophic in scale and intensity. Reports emerged that many secular people, including many Christians who did not know what was happening, hunkered down in basements and cellars to save themselves from the horrors of what they feared might come. [280]

✿✿✿†✿✿✿

In Israel 18 months earlier, Elijah mysteriously returned, as prophesied in the last book of the Old Testament. Elijah never died, God took him into heaven in a chariot of fire and a whirlwind as explained in 2 Kings.[281] Elijah's miraculous return, as Prophesied in Event #22, was explained in the book of Malachi[282] and in Allen's Major Sermon #4. Again, he returned for a two-fold purpose: The reformation of the 12 tribes of Israel and the formation of a large special group of Bible scholars.

Within six months of Elijah's arrival, he reestablished the tribal system, the 12 tribes of Israel. During this time, Elijah put out a request for the creation of a special large group of high-level Jewish scholars in the Tanakh for a special mission for Israel.

---

[280] Luke 17:30-33
[281] 2 Kings 2:11
[282] Malachi 4:5-6

His solicitation included specific limitations and criteria. As the tribal system was reformed and each Jew rediscovered which tribe they belonged to, he asked 12,000 members from each of the revived 12 tribes to join his new group of scholars. The group included 144,000 of the wisest Jewish men in the country. These men knew the Tanakh on a par with Paul's knowledge in Jesus' day. Elijah personally selected all of them, kept them fully in place as a complete group, established one year earlier.

Elijah, from the beginning of their formation, taught this group that though they did not believe Jesus is the Messiah, in order to be effective for the service God calls them for in this new world, they needed a strong working knowledge of the New Testament as well as the Old.

They all respected Elijah so for 12 months they studied and became scholars of both the Old and New Testaments. Not one of them accepted Jesus … yet.

God hardened their hearts to Jesus for a short time, the same thing He did with Saul in the days of Christ, until his time for service arrived. At the right moment, Jesus Himself, in spirit, met Saul on the road to Damascus in a bright light and temporarily blinded him for three days, as we learned earlier. Saul saw the light both literally and figuratively. On this single day Jesus arrived as an angel of light, changed Saul to faith in Him as the Messiah. Saul became Paul, the greatest and wisest of all apostles for service to Christ. Remember, Christ is not Jesus' last name; it is His title … Messiah.

Back at the lodge, Allen remembered noticing the large number of trees when they arrived in the forested area around the Dells in Wisconsin. He walked outside, thinking ahead to the time to *'look up,'* noticed a short way down the path outside the front door to the lodge lay a grassy pasture about the size of six football fields. He knew this area would offer the group a clear view of the sky.

He gathered everyone together in the main hall of the lodge and said, "With the events taking place on earth this morning I expect the *'day star'* warning to come at any moment. Everyone get your coats on so you will be prepared to walk with me the short distance to an open pasture area nearby."

Everyone put on their coats with overwhelming excitement and anticipation … great joy at the prospect of being with the Lord in moments.

✡✡✡✝✡✡✡

At about this same moment in Israel, Elijah prepared to preside over his weekly Friday gathering of the 144,000 in their large exterior Amphitheater.

Elijah knew the meaning of the signs the world experienced and knew God would ensure this group assembled at the right moment, which would soon arrive on the entire earth. The 144,000, as with most of the world, were dismayed and scared by what they saw.

Elijah told them, "God is doing amazing acts at this moment. You are all beloved by God Himself and He, through me, will give you directions shortly about His assignment for you. There is nothing to fear, God is in full control of what we are seeing."

✿✿✿†✿✿✿

In Wisconsin, the group finished putting on their coats and headed for the door. At that moment, the *'day star'* arrived in their hearts to tell them only a short time remained before the return of the Lord. Time to get prepared so they could *'look up.'*

The group, now ready, silently hurried out into the pasture. They knew about the frightening events occurring in the outside world but they remembered a key verse in the Bible saying *'if you desire to save your life you will lose it but if you are willing to lose your life you will save it.'*[283]

This verse is about the two ways a person can go in the Rapture. They knew even if what happened outside looked like it might kill them, God directed them at this moment to *'look up'* per the book of Luke because their redemption drew near.

On arrival in the pasture they all raised their arms to the heavens and looked up with mere minutes to spare before the Lord's visual return.

✿✿✿†✿✿✿

With so much terror occurring in the world environment, the most anticipated event of the day became a fleeting footnote: On this day in Israel Guy

---

[283] Luke 17:33

Terrestre planned to sign his agreement with Israel to protect them from the scourge, which continued to grow.

He pre-planned the formal signing event for weeks to happen in a televised news conference about an hour from the time the group in Wisconsin happened to 'look up.'

It was like God Himself choreographed these events. He did.

Guy paced around the hall, worried that all the events happening in the world might prevent the signing ceremony from happening. Israel, though terrified by the world events around them, feared the scourge the most, but their leaders felt reluctant to sign this agreement and stood on the verge of postponing it.

What happened in the world frightened them more but not sufficiently to sign this agreement for protection, yet. This changed a few minutes later.

✿✿✿†✿✿✿

Elijah started his standard Friday weekly practice of teaching the 144,000, who sat and waited for his words. On this day when they met in their open sky amphitheater, he knew they never anticipated what they saw in the world this day or what Elijah, their beloved leader, was about to share with them.

He said, "It's been my greatest honor to be your leader and teacher for the last year. You're now fully prepared for the mission God assigned for you. I will soon tell you the details of your mission."

Elijah already knew by the hand of God that the Rapture of the church would soon occur, so he lifted his arms to the sky and looked up.

While looking up, he said, to the 144,000, "I will be leaving shortly."

Confusion overtook the crowd. Elijah knew his flock of brethren should know what was taking place and the events that would soon happen from their studies of the New Testament over the last year. He also knew God was not ready for them to figure it out yet. He knew they wondered why he was looking up.

Elijah said, "Do you remember the Major Sermon #5 by pastor Allen Rogers we all watched together two weeks back, where he explained an event in the last days, which the Bible calls the Catching Up? He told us the Catching Up, which I will now call the Rapture, will arrive in seven events. It will not happen in an instant. An entirely different event happens in an instant. Do you remember the first event? It's the signs we see around us now. RAPTURE EVENT #1 ARRIVED.)

("The second Rapture event will be an announcement from the Lord with a shout.[284] This is the second announcement listed in Isaiah that Christ will make by Himself telling the whole world on His arrival in the clouds at first that *"the day of vengeance of our God'* has arrived, per Isaiah 61:2b. When this announcement arrives, anybody who didn't accept the Lord by this moment will enter the seven-year Tribulation. The Tribulation will begin later today by design.

---

[284] 1 Thessalonians 4:16

(AT THAT MOMENT THE SKY BRIGHTENED AND BEAUTIFUL CLOUDS BEGAN TO APPEAR.)

Elijah said, "The entire world will see this and hear the shout. Listen to Jesus."

Almost immediately (the actual shout came. Jesus announced, *"The arrival of the day of vengeance of our God."*)

Elijah paused a moment, then said, "RAPTURE EVENT #2 HAPPENED." No more options to accept Christ and avoid the Tribulation can occur after this moment. (People can accept Christ inside the Tribulation but there will be earthly consequences for doing so.) Billions however will willingly make this choice, but how?

("Your mission for God is clear. You are the 144,000 evangelists for Christ inside the Tribulation the Book of Revelation talks about. God prevented you from accepting the Lord until this moment, after which you all will accept him once you see me visually leave. Why did God do this? Because if you accepted Jesus prior to the shout, you'd all leave to heaven with me shortly. You will serve in a glorious mission. You will save more souls in the next seven years than were saved in all the 2,000 years since Christ initially ascended to His father. You are assigned to become 144,000 Pauls for service to Jesus inside the seven-year Tribulation period. Starting today, you will be indestructible. God does not want to waste one moment trying to save every soul possible during the full 70th week of Daniel ... the Tribulation.

"The seven Rapture events soon to be completed are meant to be your Damascus road conversion event. The Holy Spirit, your helper, will come upon all of you for God's glory ... Israel!"

(THE 3ᴿᴰ RAPTURE EVENT ARRIVED, THE SOUND OF THE FIRST TRUMPET, loud and heard around the whole world, at the same time. ²⁸⁵)

Elijah said, "Very shortly you're going to see God do a large miracle."

(THE 4ᵗʰ RAPTURE EVENT ARRIVED.)

Elijah said, "Every person who died in Christ since He came for His first visit will see their earthly bodies reformed. God knows where every molecule is located. (Those who are sleeping,²⁸⁶ as God calls it in the Bible, those who died on earth, who were buried, cremated, lost at sea, blown up in wars, all will be reformed and reunited with their souls as the dead will rise first into the sky.)

"They haven't changed into their eternal bodies yet; this will occur in Rapture event #7. The Bible tells us those of us alive, looking up, will not precede this group. This (first group will include living Christians who did not know to *look up.*' They hid for their lives and will die first and immediately go up with this first group. Those of us who knew prophecy and are looking up get to watch this spectacular event unfold) After all the dead finally rise the next event # 5 will occur."

After Elijah said this, the 144,000 looked off into the distance where the sky began to twinkle with what looked like thousands of fireflies. A glow or spark occurred when

---

²⁸⁵ Interesting thing about trumpets see: Numbers 10:3-6, 10:9

²⁸⁶ Sleeping, in some instances in the Bible is a term God uses for those who died here on earth before the Rapture. Their souls are in heaven already, but they are waiting for their heavenly bodies that will come in the Rapture. They get their old bodies back; we will recognize them in heaven. This all happens in the Rapture events. Examples of sleeping as being dead or "sleeping" on earth are found in: John 11:11-16, Acts 7:54-59, 1 Corinthians 50-52 and Ephesians 5:14.

a soul reunited with its reformed earthly body. These people didn't change into their heavenly bodies. This will happen shortly.

THE 5th RAPTURE EVENT WAS ABOUT TO HAPPEN.

The dead continued to rise so time grew short for Elijah to finish. Elijah said, "Every living Christian who is looking up will soon rise into the sky as the second group in their earthly bodies. The sixth event will be the final trumpet, and then in the seventh event all of us, from both the first and second groups together in the sky, will change in a moment in a twinkling of an eye into our perfect eternal bodies, perfectly healed to be with God for all eternity. Transformed Christians will not disappear in this event; we will rise into the clouds in our new eternal bodies to be seen no more, like Christ did at His initial ascension."

After he finished this statement THE 5th RAPTURE EVENT ARRIVED.

Elijah started to rise into the sky and offered his final passionate request to his men, "My brethren, Jesus comes for His church this day. I'm now leaving to be with Him. Please accept your Messiah Jesus at this moment and become the blessing for God and the Jews required in the world for the next seven years. May our Messiah Jesus guide you and bless you as you walk today into your destiny."

Elijah said his final words as he rose into the sky.

The 6th RAPTURE EVENT ARRIVED. The final deafening worldwide trumpet in the sequence of the Rapture events blared out.

THE 7th RAPTURE EVENT ARRIVED.

(All persons who'd risen and been reunited into their earthly bodies or were alive changed into their eternal bodies for the whole world to see, a highly visual event.)

(After the changing, in a twinkling, everyone in the sky was individually surrounded in brilliant light with white robes to make it clear they changed instantly.)

These events brought the 144,000 to tears of joy ... Elijah was right, Jesus is our King!

(In unison, these events so moved the 144,000 that as they watched Elijah disappear into the clouds, they all at once accepted Jesus as their Messiah. This fully installed the 144,000 mentioned in the book of Revelation for the Lord's work on day one of the Tribulation.)

✿✿✿✝✿✿✿

Back in Wisconsin, Allen's group experienced the same seven Rapture events, leaving nobody at the Lodge. His entire group of believers received the greatest blessing. They all looked up, left together in the second group, and were changed together for eternity.)

(In one magnificent variation for this group, the young children and grandchildren when changed became young adults, fully mature and recognizable to their relatives and to everyone else in the group.)

The visual Rapture bestowed one final blessing on the world. (When all the world's born-again Christians departed, millions of families and friends who did not accept Christ and thought true Christians consisted of religious fanatics became 100% sure the Jesus believers were right. Millions of them accepted Jesus at the instant of the visual departure of Christians because all members of God's family boldly shared with them future events that they believed the Bible revealed to them. The Rapture provided solid proof the Bible was right and Jesus, our Savior, is the King of kings and Lord of lords.)

With the Rapture now completed, the world erupted in full panic. The darkness that preceded the Rapture continued and grew. God was angry. Panic, horror, heart attacks and dread happened across the globe. The peace the secular world experienced earlier this morning shattered, stolen from them, as the Bible tells us,[287] taken from secular mankind. The thief in the night arrived.

For a moment at the end of the Rapture events, a short period occurred when not one believer was left in the world … a dark moment. All true believers in Jesus prior to the Tribulation were taken home with Him to safety.

✿✿✿✿✿✿✿

(The Rapture pushed Israel to a breaking point.)With the culmination of the Rapture events, the worldwide environmental dismay and darkness and the scourge getting progressively worse, an overwhelmed Israel felt it could at least control the Scourge.

---

[287] 1 Thessalonians 5:1-3, The thief steals the world's peace, it is not the Rapture.

[An hour after the end of the Rapture, Israel met as planned with Guy Terrestre and signed the seven-year covenant with him to keep the scourge away from them.]

The seven-year Biblical Time of Jacob's distress, the day of vengeance of our God, the 70th week of Daniel, God's period of 21 judgments to bring Israel, His Glory, back to Him and His Son their Messiah, which they missed and discounted at His first visit … the Tribulation began.

[There will be no peace for all the seven years as God removed it from the world on purpose at the Rapture.[288]]

The horrific seven-year reign of Guy Terrestre begins!

All hell broke loose in the remaining secular world …

DAY ONE!

If you enjoyed this book
please consider writing a review on AMAZON

Also please visit us at

www.reveretodayministries.org

---

[288] All peace in the world is removed by God prior to the Tribulation.

Rick A. Blomgren

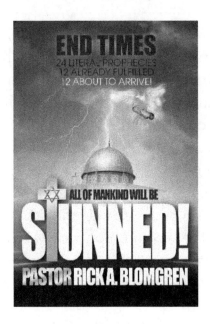

STUNNED
IS A COMPREHENSIVE STUDY GUIDE
OUTLINING, IN EXPANDED DETAIL, THE
HYPOTHESIS PROPOSED IN

THE PASTOR OF THE LAST DAYS

IN STUNNED, I OFFER ACTUAL HISTORICAL
REFERENCES INCLUDING LITERAL BIBLE TEXT AND
REFERENCES TO OVER 800 BIBLE VERSES AS SUPPORT
FOR WHAT MAY BE GOD'S PLANS FOR THE LAST
DAYS, ALL OF THEM … AMAZING!

STUNNED IS AVAILABLE ON **AMAZON BOOKS**,
TYPE IN
STUNNED BLOMGREN

ORDER YOUR COPY!

OF THIS HELPFUL 358 PAGE STUDY GUIDE TODAY ☺

236

GOD'S 24 EVENT END TIMES ROAD MAP

12 PROPHECIES COMPLETED OR ONGOING [289]

1. TWO MAJOR BIRTH PAINS, WWI, AND WWII
2. PREPARING THE LAND OF ISRAEL FOR THE JEWS
3. UNITED NATIONS FORMS
4. REBIRTH OF THE NEW STATE OF ISRAEL – **SUPER SIGN #1**
5. RETURN OF THE JEWS TO THE HOLY LAND
6. CAPTURE OF JERUSALEM
7. THE FALLING AWAY (APOSTASY)
8. INCREASE IN TRAVEL AND KNOWLEDGE
9. RISE OF ANTI-SEMITISM
10. MARK OF THE BEAST (TECHNOLOGY)
11. ISRAEL DWELLING SECURELY
12. GAZA ABANDONED

12 PROPHECIES THAT WILL HAPPEN IN SHORT ORDER [290]

13. GOD'S NEXT PROPHECY: EZEKIEL 38 & 39 – **SUPER SIGN #2**
14. FIRST STAGE OF CONVERSION OF THE JEWS
15. REBUILDING OF BABYLON (Iraq, not Rome)
16. ONE WORLD GOVERNMENT AND ECONOMY
17. ONE WORLD CHURCH AND FALSE PROPHET
18. BUILDING OF THE THIRD TEMPLE IN JERUSALEM
19. WORLD GOVERNMENT BREAKS INTO 10 KINGDOMS
20. RISE OF THE ANTICHRIST (after the 10 kingdoms)
21. TIME OF PEACE & SAFETY IN THE UNBELIEVING WORLD
22. THE APPEARANCE OF ELIJAH
23. FEAR, SCOURGE, THE ANTICHRIST, AND HIS COVENANT
24. THE DAY OF THE VISUAL RAPTURE – **SUPER SIGN #3**

For a detailed printout copy of this list

with biblical references for each event, visit our website at:

www.reveretodayministries.org

Look for the reference **ROAD MAP.**

---

[289] *Stunned,* 2015, Blomgren, pages 32-42 for comprehensive biblical detail.
[290] *Stunned,* 2015, Blomgren, pages 42-87 for comprehensive biblical detail

Rick A. Blomgren

List of Acts